ALL THE WORLD'S ANIMALS
FISHES

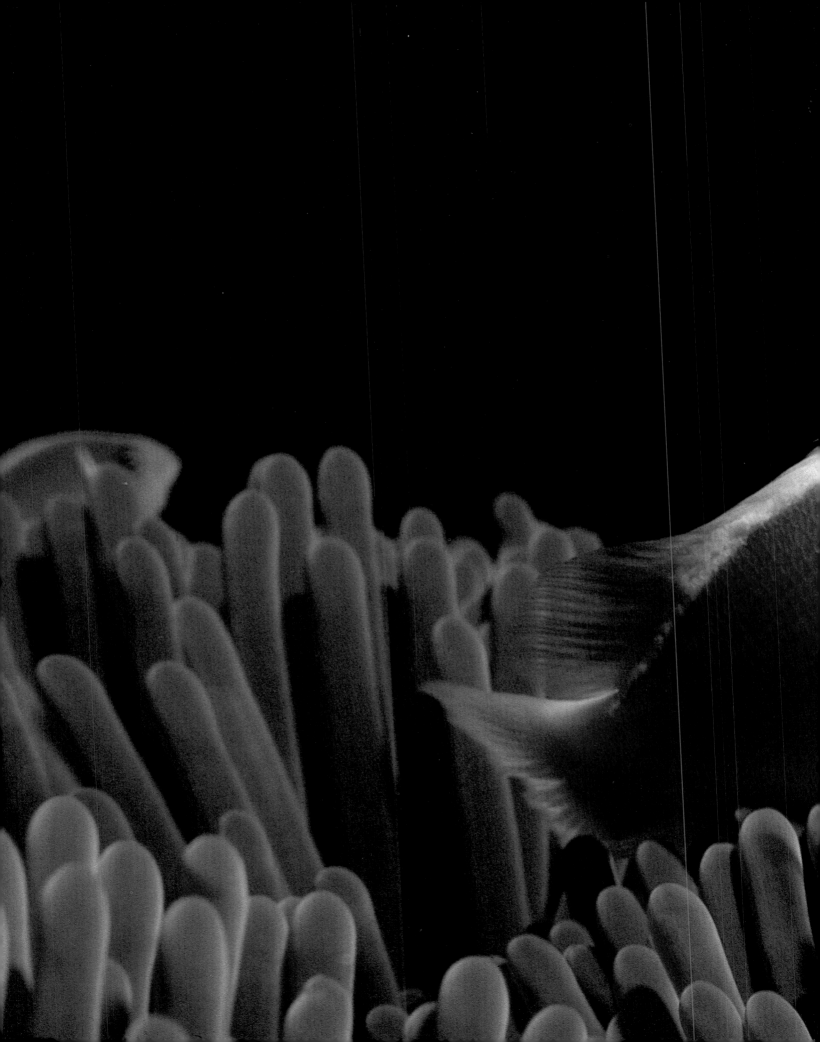

ALL THE WORLD'S ANIMALS

FISHES

TORSTAR BOOKS
New York · Toronto

CONTRIBUTORS

RGB   Roland G. Bailey BSc PhD
Chelsea College
University of London
England

KEB   Keith E. Banister PhD
British Museum
(Natural History)
London, England

BB   Bernice Brewster BSc
British Museum
(Natural History)
London, England

GD   Guido Dingerkus BS MS
MPhil PhD
American Museum of Natural
History
New York, USA

GJH   Gordon J. Howes MIBiol
British Museum
(Natural History)
London, England

RMcD   Bob McDowall MSc PhD
Ministry of Agriculture and
Fisheries
Christchurch
New Zealand

LP   Lynne Parenti
California Academy of
Sciences
San Francisco, USA

JEM   John E. McCosker BA PhD
Steinhart Aquarium
California Academy of Sciences
San Francisco, USA

ALL THE WORLD'S ANIMALS
FISHES

TORSTAR BOOKS INC.
41 Madison Avenue, Suite 2900, New York, NY 10010.

Project Editor: Graham Bateman
Editors: Bill MacKeith, Robert Peberdy
Art Editor: Jerry Burman
Art Assistant: Carol Wells

Picture Research: Alison Renney
Production: Clive Sparling
Design: Chris Munday, Andrew Lawson
Index: Barbara James

Originally planned and produced by:
Equinox (Oxford) Ltd
Littlegate House, St Ebbe's Street, Oxford OX1 1SQ, England.

On the cover: Sergeant Major fish *Page 1:* Atlantic Salmon
Pages 2–3: Philippine clown fish *Pages 4–5:* Lion fish
Pages 6–7: Snappers *Pages 8–9:* Coral trout with cleaver fish

9 8 7 6 5 4 3 2 1

Printed in Belgium

Editors
Dr Keith Banister
British Museum (Natural History),
London, England.

Dr Andrew Campbell
Queen Mary College,
University of London, England.

Advisory Editors
Professor Fu-Shiang Chia
The University of Alberta, Edmonton,
Canada.

Dr John E. McCosker
Steinhart Aquarium, California Academy
of Sciences, San Francisco, USA.

Dr R. M. McDowall
Ministry of Agriculture and Fisheries,
Christchurch, New Zealand.

Artwork panels and diagrams
S. S. Driver
Richard Lewington
Richard Gorringe

Mick Loates
Denys Ovenden
Norman Weaver

Library of Congress Cataloging in Publication Data

Main entry under title:

Fishes.

  (All the world's animals)
  Bibliography: p.
  Includes index.
  1. Fishes.   I. Series.
QL617.F55   1986   597   86–1305
ISBN 0–920269–79–6

ISBN 0–920269–72–9 (Series: All the World's Animals)
ISBN 0–920269–79–6 (Fishes)

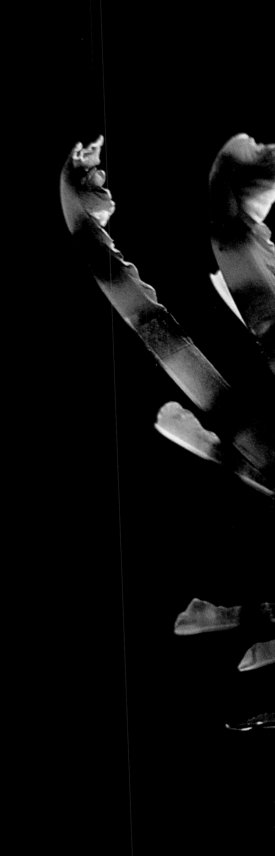

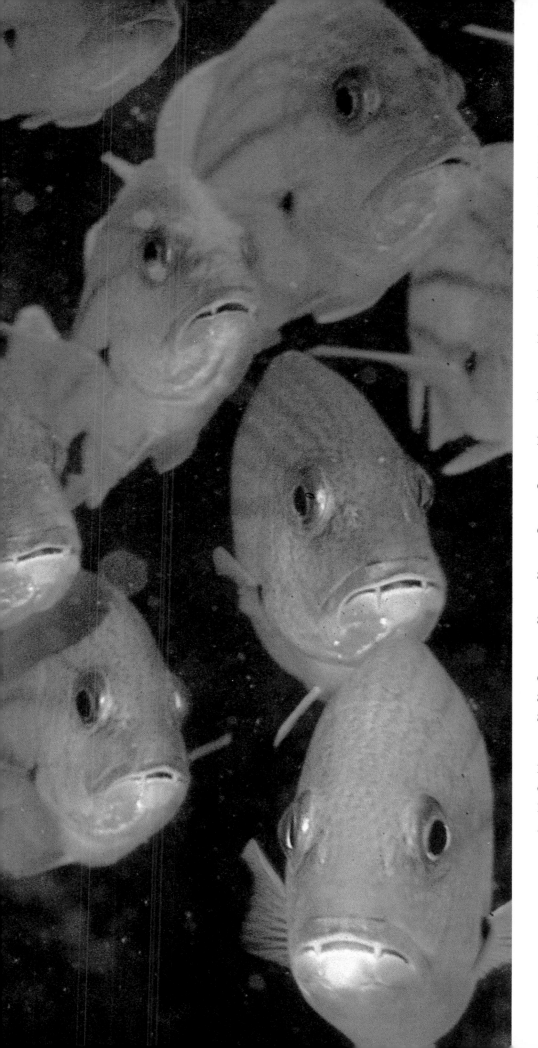

CONTENTS

FOREWORD

About four hundred million years ago the first creatures that could truly be called fishes swam in the earth's ancient seas. Today, as a result of millennia of diversification, more than twenty thousand clearly defined fish species, in a multitude of shapes and sizes, inhabit the world's waters. These range from the tiniest dwarf goby, measuring half an inch, to the largest whale shark, which is more than forty feet from end to end. Appearances vary too. Drab, blind, even eyeless fishes live in the cold lightless depths of subterranean caves, while brightly colored clown fishes dwell amid sea anemone tentacles in the warm shallow waters of the tropics.

The rich variety of their adaptations to a subtly changing environment makes fishes an extraordinary and often bizarre collection of creatures. From the brilliant luminosity of the flashlight fish to the unerring accuracy of the archer fishes as they shoot unsuspecting insects with drops of water, the piscatorial world often demonstrates the extremes of Nature's versatility. And while some species, such as herrings, are represented by countless millions of individuals, others, such as the coelacanth, just manage to survive precariously with a few small breeding groups.

Fishes is an exciting aquatic adventure into watery realms, where the shifting patterns of light and shade harbor glorious colors and astonishing antics. The startling anatomies and curious behavior of our marine and freshwater relatives are brought to life on terra firma by a lucid text illustrated with beautiful photographs and detailed color drawings.

How this book is organized

Because there are so many species of fishes there is an extensive literature reporting the research that has been conducted on many aspects of their biology, anatomy, behavior and relationships. What the contributors have aimed to do in this volume is to distill their knowledge to give the reader a flavor of the essence of fishes. It is inevitable in the space available that there are gaps, but these are largely of detail, not of import. As far as possible the major biological principles are each covered by an example. This may not necessarily be a familiar one, but will nonetheless illustrate the general point.

Most of the text deals with the four major living classes of fishes (lampreys, hagfishes, jawed fishes, jawless fishes). There is no universally accepted classification for fishes. Rather than produce a misleading classification that might be assumed to be definitive, our text stresses many of the problems. We felt it better to admit the current state of uncertainty and confusion, to admit that there are profound disagreements between different schools of ichthyological thought and to admit that there is much about which we are ignorant.

The present survey proceeds with articles covering a group of closely related species, the length of each reflecting the importance and interest of the group and to some extent the number of species in the group. Each article is prefaced by a fact panel which provides a digest of information, covering the number of species, genera and families as well as their distribution and size range. Outline drawings of examples from key families are also provided to help the reader visualize what the fishes look like. For large groups this information is consolidated in a separate table. Where possible, common names are used in the fact boxes or tables. However, some groups (and the great majority of species) have no common names, or these names vary from country to country, hence the universally accepted scientific name for the group has to be used. This may seem unnecessarily cumbersome but it was the only way to provide a peg on which to hang the group. One value of scientific names is that the ending of many informs the reader of the hierarchy of the group being discussed; this system is explained in "What Is a Fish?"

As well as the outline drawings there are spreads of color illustrations. Most of these have been drawn from actual specimens in an attempt to avoid perpetuating errors in the literature. Because fishes vary considerably in size it is not possible to show them to scale in the plates. An approximate size for each fish is given in the captions. Relevant line drawings of important anatomical features are also included. Color photographs drawn from sources worldwide complement and enhance the text and the other artwork. Here again, rarely illustrated species have been chosen.

In addition to the sequence of systematic articles there are numerous special features. These are multidisciplinary and deal with unrelated fishes. After all, a trawler does not selectively catch fishes of just one species! Thus concepts dealing with the associations of fishes with ourselves, or with habits common to different groups of fishes, transcend the natural categories. Here are articles on the problems posed for fishes that live on land, and their solutions; on the difficulty of living in caves; and on bioluminescence. Aspects and consequences of our interaction with fishes as food and in captivity is largely historical, the treatment of endangered fishes and the future of fishes is concerned with what humans have done to fish species and whether we will learn from the mistakes of yesterday to make a better tomorrow.

WHAT IS A FISH?

Jawless fishes
Classes: Cephalaspidomorphi, Myxini
Two or four families: 12 or 17 genera: 72 species.

Lampreys
Class: Cephalaspidomorphi
Order: Petromyzontiformes.
About forty species in 6 or 11 genera and
1 or 3 families.

Hagfishes
Class: Myxini
Order: Myxiniformes.
About thirty-two species in 6 genera of the family
Myxinidae.

Bony fishes
Class: Osteichthyes
Four hundred and twenty families: 3,700 genera:
about 20,750 species.

Sturgeons and paddlefishes
Order: Acipenseriformes
Twenty-seven species in 6 genera and 2 families.

Bowfin and garfishes
Families: Amiidae, Lepisosteidae
Eight species in 3 genera.

Tarpons, eels and notacanths
Superorder: Elopomorpha
About six hundred and thirty-two species in about 160
genera and about 30 families.

Herrings, anchovies and allies
Superorder: Clupeomorpha
About three hundred and forty-two species in
68 genera and 4 families.
Includes: **herring** (*Clupea harengus*).

Bony tongues and allies
Superorder: Osteoglossomorpha
About one hundred and sixteen species in
26 genera and 6 families.

Pike, salmon, argentines and allies
Order: Salmoniformes
Over three hundred species in 80 genera and
17 families.
Includes: **argentines** (family Argentinidae), **Brown trout**
(*Salmo trutta*).

Bristle mouths and allies
Order: Stomiiformes
About two hundred and fifty species in over
50 genera and about 9 families.

IN all probability life started in our planet's waters about 3,000 million years ago. For a very long time not much seems to have happened. The first known multicellular invertebrates occur about 600 million years ago. After a much shorter interval (in geological terms), about 120 million years, the first aquatic vertebrates, the fishes, appeared. From these innovative fish groups arose the animals most familiar to us today—birds, mammals and especially ourselves.

Over half of the vertebrates alive today are these masters of the water—the fishes. They do just about everything that the other vertebrates do and also have many unique attributes. Only fishes, for example, make their own light (see p72), produce electricity, have complete parasitism (see p106) as well as having the largest increase in volume from hatching to adulthood.

Different people have different impressions of fish. To some the epitome of the fish is the sharp-toothed shark, elegantly and effortlessly hunting its prey in the sea. To others fish are small, pretty animals giving some point to the aquarium in the home. For anglers, fish are a cunning quarry to be outwitted and caught. For the commercial fishermen fish are a mass of slimy silvery bodies being hauled on board the vessel: the more fish, the more money. Biologists regard fish as representing a mass of problems concerning evolution, behavior and form, the study of which provides more questions than answers.

It is the very diversity of fishes, the large number of species and the huge numbers of individuals of some species that make them so interesting, instructive and useful to us.

It is easy to see that the huge shoals (provided they are maintained by careful management) form a valuable food resource for us and other animals, but it is not so generally realized that research is being conducted on the use of the poison from fish spines in surgical techniques. In making transplants of hearts and lungs in humans there are problems of tissue rejection: how much might we learn from the fusion of the male angler fish onto the female's body? (See p106.) They seemingly have no rejection problems. Studies on a few small species of fish that exist as eyed surface forms and eyeless cave forms may help us to understand the relationship between the genetic code and the environment (see p92). There are many similar examples.

Fish, then, are many things to many people and for millennia they have fascinated mankind in many ways, not least because they have conquered an environment that is to us alien. Yet all these associations between humans and fish beg the most vital question of all.

▲ **Elegant, effortless hunters,** sharks are a group of fishes that lack a bony skeleton. Their graceful, powerful bodies have a skeleton of flexible gristle-like substance called cartilage. Their gill slits open separately to the outside and are not covered by an operculum (cover). Their teeth are constantly replaced and there is a spiral valve in the intestine to increase the absorptive area. This is the Gray reef shark (*Carcharhinus amblyrhynchus*).

▶ **Calculating predators of the deep,** deep-sea angler fishes are commonest in lightless waters. Above the mouth is a modified dorsal fin ray (the illicium) which terminates in a luminous lure (the esca). With this they entice their prey. Some species also have an elaborate chin barbel (its function is uncertain). Most are small fishes (there is little food in the deep sea) but in one species, *Ceratias hoelboelli*, the females can grow to 3.3ft (1m) long.

Lizard fishes and lantern fishes

Orders: Aulopiformes, Myctophiformes
About four hundred and forty species in about 75 genera and about 13 families.

Characins, catfishes, carps and milk fishes

Superorder: Ostariophysi
About six thousand species in at least 907 genera and 50 families.
Includes: **carp** (*Cyprinus carpio*), **goldfish** (*Carrasius auratus*).

Beard fishes, cling fishes, cods, angler fishes and allies

Superorder: Paracanthopterygii
About one thousand one hundred species in about 200 genera, 30 families and 6 orders.
Includes: **rat-tails** or **grenadiers** (family Macrouridae).

Silversides, killifishes, ricefishes and allies

Series: Atherinomorpha
Superorder: Acanthopterygii.
About one thousand species in about 165 genera, 21 families, 2 orders and 1 division.
Includes: **Devil's Hole pupfish** (*Cyprinodon diabolis*).

Spiny-finned fishes

Series: Percomorpha
Superorder: Acanthopterygii.
About ten thousand five hundred species in 2,000 genera, 230 families and 11 orders.
Includes: **Nile perch** (*Lates niloticus*), **Red mullet** (*Mullus surmuletus*).

Bichirs, coelacanth and lungfishes

Orders: Polypteriformes, Coelacanthiformes; superorder: Ceratodontimorpha
Seventeen species in 6 genera, 4 or 5 families and 4 orders.

Cartilaginous fishes

Class: Chondrichthyes
Thirty-one families: 130 genera: about 711 species.

Sharks

Subclass Selachii
About three hundred and seventy species in 74 genera, 21 families and 12 orders.

Skates and rays

Order: Batiformes
About three hundred and eighteen species in 50 genera and 7 families.

Chimaeras

Subclass: Holocephali
About twenty-three species in 6 genera, 3 families and the order Chimaeriformes.

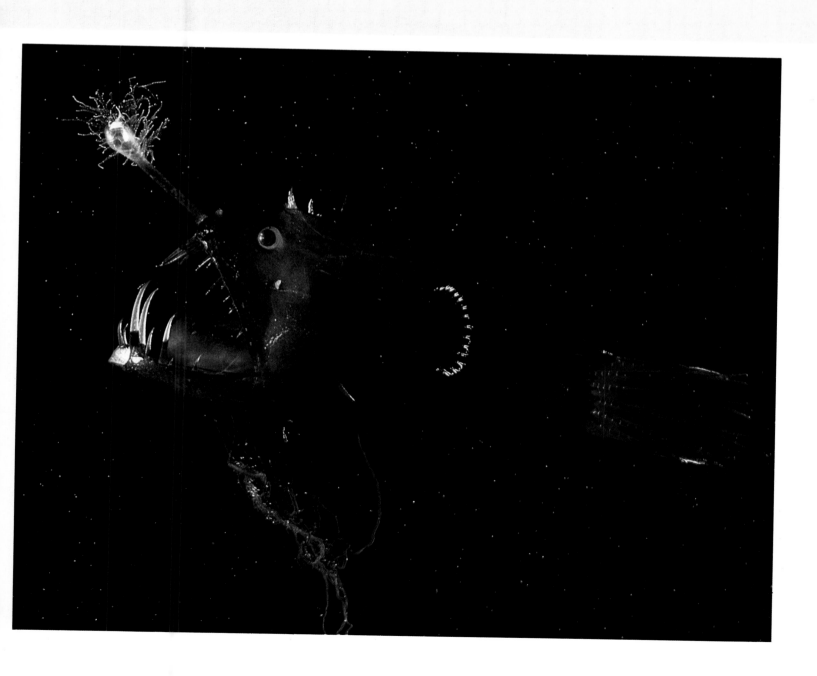

What is a fish?

There is no such thing as a fish. "Fish" is simply a shorthand notation for an aquatic vertebrate that is not a mammal, a turtle or anything else. There are four quite separate groups of fish, not closely related to one another. Lumping these four groups together under the heading fish is like lumping all flying vertebrates, ie bats (mammals), birds and even the flying lizard under the heading "birds" just because they all fly. The relationship between a lamprey and a shark is no closer than that between a salamander and a camel.

However, the centuries of acceptance of "fish" as a descriptive term dictate that, for convenience, it will be used here. But remember that using the word fish for the four different living groups is equivalent to referring to all other vertebrates as tetrapods, even if some have subsequently lost or modified their legs.

The four living groups consist of two groups of jawless fishes, the hagfishes and the lampreys, and two groups with jaws, the cartilaginous fishes (sharks and rays) and the bony fishes (all the rest). There are also two other groups that are now extinct.

The four living groups differ widely in their numbers of species. There are about 32 species of hagfish and about 40 of lamprey. Today the jawed fishes dominate: the sharks, rays and chimaeras comprise about 700 species while the greatest flowering is in the bony fishes with over 20,000 species.

A brief history of the major groups

The first identifiable remains of fishes are small, broken and crushed plates in rocks of the middle Ordovician era 460–480 million years ago. (Possible traces from the upper Cambrian era, more than 500 million years ago, have not yet been confirmed.) These plates represent parts of the bony external armor of jawless fishes. Although none of the *living* jawless fishes has any external protection, large defensive head-shields were not uncommon in the early forms. But it is not known what the overall body shape of the first known fishes was like.

About 150 million years after they first appeared, the jawless fishes radiated into many widely varying forms, quite unlike the eel-like forms alive today. In some species of the Devonian era (400–350 million years ago) the armor was reduced to a series of thin rods allowing greater flexibility of the body. In one poorly known group, represented now by mere shadowy outlines on rocks, the armor consisted solely of tiny isolated tubercles (nodules).

Most of these Devonian jawless fishes were small. An exception are the pteraspids, fishes with the front half of the body covered with a massive plate, often with a backward pointing spine. They could reach 5ft (1.5m) in length. The cephalaspids, with their shield-shaped head plates, are a group well known from fossils in the Old Red Sandstone. A fortunate discovery of some well-preserved cephalaspids buried in fine mud enabled, with careful preparation, the course of their nerves and blood vessels to be discovered.

The first recognizable fossil lampreys have been found in Carboniferous (Penn-

The Ranking of Fishes

The ranking of a fish or a group of fishes (a taxon) within the hierarchy is indicated by the ending of the group name. These endings are uniform up to and including order, but there is little standardization for higher categories, despite attempts having been made to introduce it. Taking as an example the now ubiquitous carp, *Cyprinus carpio*, we have:

carpio	the trivial name of that species
Cyprinus	genus, which includes other species
Cyprinidae	family, which includes many genera, eg *Cyprinus, Pimephales, Tribolodon*
Cyprinoidei	suborder, which includes other families, eg Cobitidae (loaches)
Cypriniformes	order, which contains the other suborders, eg Charcoidei (characins)
Ostariophysi	superorder, which contains other orders, eg Siluriformes (catfishes)

Although there are yet higher categories, as well as others inserted between the stages listed above, they tend to be used only in a rather specialized fashion.

Great care must be taken when expressing some of these categories by using informal names based on scientific names. Cyprinoids, for example, comprise all the species in six families of the suborder Cyprinoidei (Cyprinidae, Psilorhynchidae, Gyrinocheilidae, Homalopteridae, Cobitidae and Catostomidae) whereas cyprinids refers solely to the species in the one family Cyprinidae.

BODY PLAN OF FISH

The four extant classes of fishes are, in their way, as different from each other as are the classes of land vertebrates. Some of these differences, although fundamental, concern details of anatomy; other differences are more obvious. It must be remembered that in those classes containing large numbers of species (especially the bony fishes) there are fishes whose features make them exceptional to the generalizations given opposite. Such is the nature of the diverse creatures grouped together under the title "Fishes."

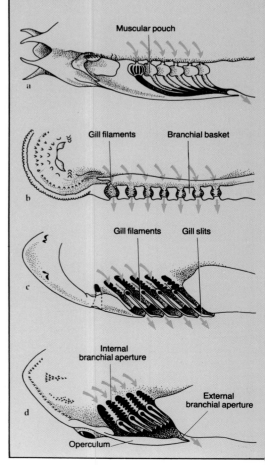

▼ **Gill structures in fishes.** (a) In the hagfishes water passes through a series of muscular pouches before it leaves through a single common opening. (b) In the lampreys each gill has a separate opening to the outside and the gills are supported by an elaborate cartilaginous structure called the branchial basket. (c) In the living chondrichthyes (sharks, skates and chimaeras) the gills (except in the chimaeras) primitively open directly to the outside via five slits. (In the chimaeras an operculum or cover is developed.) (d) In bony fishes the gills are protected externally by a bony operculum (cover).

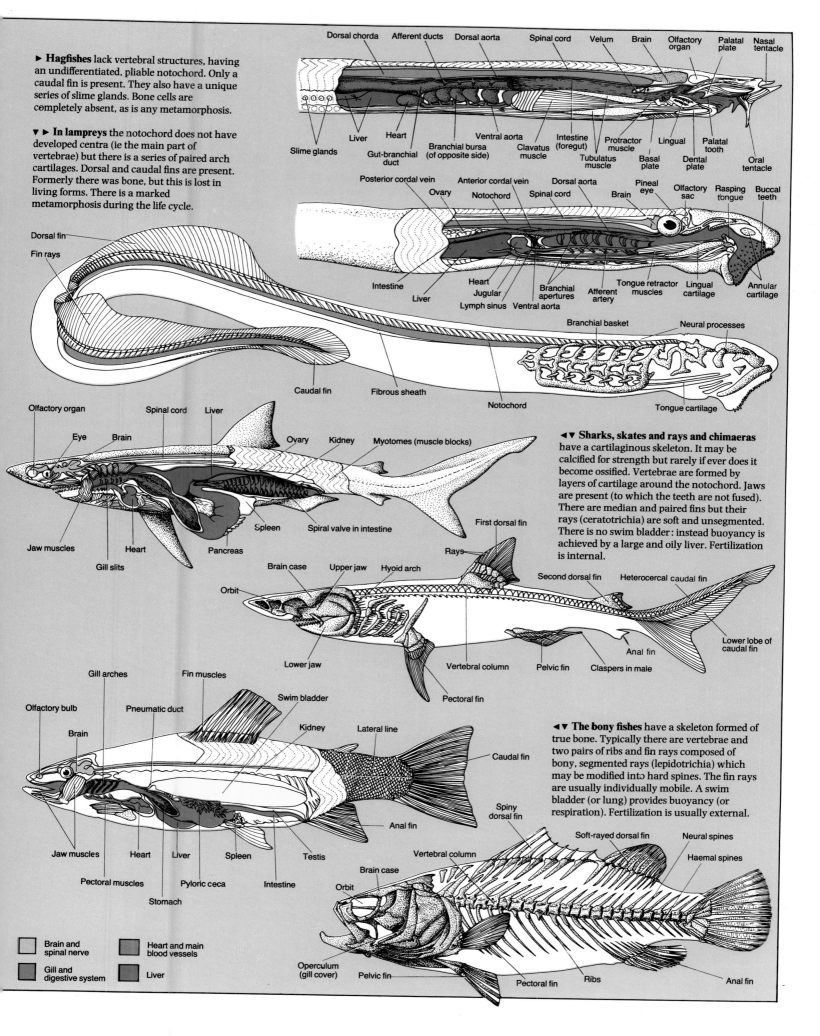

▶ **Hagfishes** lack vertebral structures, having an undifferentiated, pliable notochord. Only a caudal fin is present. They also have a unique series of slime glands. Bone cells are completely absent, as is any metamorphosis.

▼ ▶ **In lampreys** the notochord does not have developed centra (ie the main part of vertebrae) but there is a series of paired arch cartilages. Dorsal and caudal fins are present. Formerly there was bone, but this is lost in living forms. There is a marked metamorphosis during the life cycle.

Dorsal fin
Fin rays
Caudal fin
Fibrous sheath
Notochord

Dorsal chorda
Afferent ducts
Dorsal aorta
Spinal cord
Velum
Brain
Olfactory organ
Palatal plate
Nasal tentacle
Slime glands
Liver
Heart
Gut-branchial duct
Branchial bursa (of opposite side)
Ventral aorta
Clavatus muscle
Intestine (foregut)
Protractor muscle
Tubulatus muscle
Lingual
Basal plate
Palatal tooth
Dental plate
Oral tentacle

Posterior cordal vein
Anterior cordal vein
Dorsal aorta
Pineal eye
Olfactory sac
Rasping tongue
Buccal teeth
Ovary
Notochord
Spinal cord
Brain
Intestine
Liver
Heart
Jugular
Lymph sinus
Branchial apertures
Ventral aorta
Afferent artery
Tongue retractor muscles
Lingual cartilage
Annular cartilage
Branchial basket
Neural processes
Tongue cartilage

Sharks, skates and rays and chimaeras have a cartilaginous skeleton. It may be calcified for strength but rarely if ever does it become ossified. Vertebrae are formed by layers of cartilage around the notochord. Jaws are present (to which the teeth are not fused). There are median and paired fins but their rays (ceratotrichia) are soft and unsegmented. There is no swim bladder: instead buoyancy is achieved by a large and oily liver. Fertilization is internal.

Olfactory organ
Eye
Brain
Spinal cord
Liver
Ovary
Kidney
Myotomes (muscle blocks)
Jaw muscles
Heart
Gill slits
Spleen
Pancreas
Spiral valve in intestine

Brain case
Upper jaw
Hyoid arch
Orbit
Lower jaw
Vertebral column
Pelvic fin
Pectoral fin
Claspers in male
First dorsal fin
Rays
Second dorsal fin
Heterocercal caudal fin
Anal fin
Lower lobe of caudal fin

◀ ▼ **The bony fishes** have a skeleton formed of true bone. Typically there are vertebrae and two pairs of ribs and fin rays composed of bony, segmented rays (lepidotrichia) which may be modified into hard spines. The fin rays are usually individually mobile. A swim bladder (or lung) provides buoyancy (or respiration). Fertilization is usually external.

Olfactory bulb
Gill arches
Fin muscles
Brain
Pneumatic duct
Swim bladder
Kidney
Lateral line
Caudal fin
Jaw muscles
Heart
Liver
Spleen
Testis
Anal fin
Pectoral muscles
Pyloric ceca
Intestine
Stomach
Spiny dorsal fin
Vertebral column
Brain case
Orbit
Operculum (gill cover)
Pelvic fin
Pectoral fin
Ribs
Soft-rayed dorsal fin
Neural spines
Haemal spines
Anal fin

Brain and spinal nerve
Gill and digestive system
Heart and main blood vessels
Liver

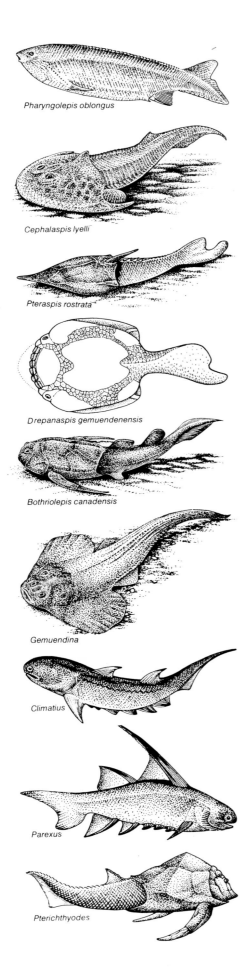

Pharyngolepis oblongus

Cephalaspis lyelli

Pteraspis rostrata

Drepanaspis gemuendenensis

Bothriolepis canadensis

Gemuendina

Climatius

Parexus

Pterichthyodes

sylvanian) rocks of Illinois, USA (dating from 325–280 million years ago). So far no indisputable fossil hagfishes have been found.

The earliest of the true jawed fishes were the acanthodians. Spines belonging to this group of large-eyed, scaled fishes have been reported from rocks 440 million years old. They probably hunted by sight in the upper layers of the waters. Some of the largest species which grew to over 6.5ft (2m) long have jaws that suggest they were active predators, much like sharks today. The majority of the acanthodians, though, were small fishes. The earliest acanthodians were marine; the later species lived in fresh water.

Acanthodians had bone, ganoid scales and a stout spine in front of each fin except the caudal. Most species had a row of spines between the pectoral and pelvic fins. The tail was shark-like (heterocercal), ie the upper lobe was longer than the lower. The tail shape and the presence of spines have led to them being called spiny sharks, despite the presence of bone and scales. Recent research has suggested that they may, however, be more closely related to the bony fishes. They never evolved flattened or bottom-living forms. One hundred and fifty million years after they appeared they became extinct.

The other group of extinct fishes is the placoderms, a bizarre class which may be related to sharks, or to bony fishes, or to both or to all other jawed fishes; no one knows for certain. The front half of their body was enclosed in bony plates, formed into a head shield which articulated with the trunk shield. Most had depressed bodies and lived on the bottom. One order, however, the arthrodires, were probably fast-swimming active predators growing to 20ft (6m) long. They probably paralleled the living sharks in the same way that the very depressed rhenanids paralleled rays and skates. Another group of placoderms, the antiarchs, are among the strangest fishes that have ever evolved. About 1ft (30cm) long, they had an armor-plated trunk which was triangular in cross section. The eyes were very small and placed close together on the top of the head. The "pectoral fins" are most extraordinary and unique among vertebrates. Whereas all other vertebrates had developed an internal skeleton, the "pectoral fin" of these antiarchs had changed to a crustacean-like condition. The "fins" resemble the legs of a lobster, ie a tube of jointed bony plates worked internally by muscles. The function of these appendages is unknown, but they may have been used

to drag the fish slowly over mud or rocks. The antiarchs also have a pair of internal sacs, which have been interpreted as lungs. In another group of placoderms, the ptyctodontids, a little can be surmised about their reproduction. The pelvic fins show sexual dimorphism, those of the males being enlarged into shark-like claspers. From this it is assumed that fertilization was internal.

Most of the early, and a few of the later, placoderms lived in fresh water; the rest, including the delightful antiarchs, were marine. This enigmatic group appeared about 400 million years ago and died out about 70 million years later.

History of fish in captivity
Seventy percent of the earth's surface is covered with water which, unlike the land surface, offers a three-dimensional living space, very little of which is devoid of fish life. The overall contribution that fish make to the total vertebrate biomass is therefore considerable. Yet because they are not as obvious a part of the environment as are birds and mammals they have not been as generally appreciated as they deserve, though man has been interested in them for at least 4,000 years.

It is not known when fishes were first kept in captivity; nor is the motive for doing this known, although it may be surmised that it was to provide an easily obtainable source of fresh food rather than for aesthetic purposes. Around 4,000 years ago the Middle East in general, and the fertile crescent of the Tigris and Euphrates in particular, were much wetter and more fertile than now. It was in this period that the first identifiable fish ponds were built by the Sumerians in their temples. The Assyrians and other races followed a little later. It is possible that fishes left behind and surviving in natural depressions after a flood may well have suggested the idea. It is not known which fishes were kept in the fertile crescent ponds. The Assyrians depicted fishes on their coins, but diagrammatically, so we cannot identify them.

The story is quite different with the Egyptians. Their high standard of representational art has enabled the fishes in their ponds to be identified. Even more conveniently they mummified some of their important species so that the accuracy of the drawings can be checked. Various species of "*Tilapia*" (still a much valued food fish in the region), Nile perch and *Mormyrus* are among those present. The Egyptians added a new dimension to the functional aspect of fish ponds, that of recreation. Murals depict

fishing with a rod and line, which must have been for fun because it is not as efficient as netting for catching fish in commercial quantities. The Egyptians also worshiped their fish.

The Roman Marcus Terentius Varro (116–27 BC) wrote in his book *De re rustica* of two kinds of fish ponds: there were freshwater ponds (*dulces*) kept by the peasantry for food and profit, and salt-water ponds (*maritimae* or *sales*) which were only owned by wealthy aristocrats who used them to entertain guests. Red mullet were especially favored as the color changes of the dying fish were admired by guests before the fish was

cooked and eaten. Large moray eels were also kept and in the most extreme examples they were decorated with jewelry and fed on unwanted or errant slaves. There is also a record of 6,000 morays being on show at an imperial banquet. Although the Romans had a glass technology there is no record of any form of aquarium having been constructed. The Romans' involvement with fish was not totally for show. They explored fish culture methods and were known to have transported fertilized fish eggs. They may well have externally fertilized the eggs by stripping the fish.

Records of fishes are few in the western

world after the fall of the Roman Empire. Indeed, during the Dark Ages there are few records of anything. Cassiodorus (AD c.490–c.585) mentioned that live carp were taken from the Danube to the Goth king Theodoric at Ravenna in Italy. Charlemagne marketed the live fishes he kept in ponds.

The tradition had doubtless been kept alive, however, by clergy and nobles. It is stated in Domesday Book (1086) that the Abbot of St Edmund's had fish ponds providing fresh food for the monastery table and that Robert Malet of Yorkshire had 20 ponds taxed to the value of 20 eels. Stew ponds were common in monasteries during the Middle Ages and were regarded as essential as the church forbade the eating of meat on Friday. The word stew comes from the Old French *estui*, meaning to confine, and does not allude to the means of preparation of the fish for consumption.

Modern-style aquaria were developed in the first half of the 19th century. At a meeting of the British Association for the Advancement of Science in 1833 it was shown that aquatic plants absorbed carbon dioxide and emitted oxygen thereby benefiting the fish. The first attempt at keeping marine fish alive and the water healthy by the use of plants was made by Mrs Thynne in 1846. Only six years later came the first public aquarium of any size, built in the Zoological Gardens in London. In late Victorian times, as now, many homes had aquaria and the invention of the heater and thermostat latterly allowed more exotic fishes to be kept.

But it is to the humblest of all aquarium fishes, the goldfish, that we now return. This species is native to China and has been bred for its beauty for over 4,500 years. In 475 BC Fan Lai wrote that carp culture had been associated with silkworm culture—the fish feeding on the feces—since 2689 BC. About 2000 BC the Chinese were, according to fishery experts, artificially hatching fish eggs. Red goldfish were noted in AD 350 and during the T'ang dynasty (about AD 650) gold-colored fish-shaped badges were a symbol of high office. By the 10th century elementary medicines for fish were available. Poplar bark was advocated for removing fish lice from goldfish.

In the wild state goldfish are brown, but when first brought into Britain (probably in 1691) gold, red, white and mottled varieties were available. They certainly were in 1728 when the merchant and economist Sir Matthew Dekker imported a great number and distributed them to many country houses.

They reached America in the 18th century and are now one of the most familiar fishes. Next time you see them in suspended plastic bags as prizes at a fair, think on their long history, for they are not actually such humble fish but fish of a long pedigree.

Endangered fishes

In 1982 the Fish and Wildlife Service of the USA proposed the removal of the Blue pike (*Stizostedion vitreum glaucum*) and the Longjaw cisco (*Coregonus alpenae*) from the American "List of Endangered and Threatened Wildlife." Not because their numbers had recovered to their former abundance but because they were deemed extinct. The Blue pike, which formerly lived in the Niagara River and Lakes Erie and Ontario, had not been seen since the early 1960s. The Longjaw cisco, from Lakes Michigan, Huron and Erie, was last reported in 1967. What caused their final disappearance after thousands of years of successful survival? Both species, directly and via their food chain, were severely hit by pollution and, on top of that, the Longjaw cisco in particular suffered from predation by parasitic lampreys that came into its habitat when the Welland Canal was built (see p26).

In South Africa a small minnow, now called *Oreodaimon quathlambae*, was des-

◀▲ **Sea fish for public view.** During the latter half of the 19th century public aquaria were popular spectacles as well as meeting places. The public acquarium, LEFT, was constructed for the 1867 Paris exhibition.

In contrast a modern aquarium, such as the Fish Roundabout at the Steinhart Aquarium in San Francisco ABOVE, has a totally different appearance and function: there is a strong emphasis on facilitating the conservation and reproduction of endangered species.

◀ **Ornamental fishes,** some of the cultivated varieties of goldfish. Centuries of intensive breeding have led to the development of varieties of fish that could not live in the wild.

▼ **Danger in Death Valley.** Some fish now live throughout the world. Others survive only in particular places and habitats. The Devil's Hole pupfish seen here is restricted to a tiny water-filled hole in the floor of Death Valley, USA. Its future depends on the maintenance of the water table. Further pumping of water in the region will destroy its food supply.

cribed in 1938. A few years later it was extinct in its original locality in Natal. No canals had been dug, pollution was minimal, but an exotic species, the Brown trout (*Salmo trutta*), had been introduced to provide familiar sport for the expatriates. Small trout ate the same food as *Oreodaimon* and large trout ate the *Oreodaimon*; result, no *Oreodaimon* in the Umkomazana river. Luckily late in the 1970s a small population was discovered living above a waterfall in the Drakensberg mountains. The fall had prevented the spread of trout, but they had recently been transplanted above the falls. Although this population is protected as far as possible from predation, a more serious threat to its survival is the overgrazing of the land adjoining the river, causing the silting up of the river and changes in the river's flow.

In parts of Malaysia, Sri Lanka and in Lake Malawi some of the more brightly colored freshwater fishes are becoming harder and harder to find. In these cases, on top of any other pressures that may exist, the numbers have fallen because of extensive collecting for the aquarium trade and concomitant environmental damage.

Formerly, large parts of the American southwest were covered with extensive lakes. With post-Pleistocene desiccation (ie about 100,000 years ago) the lakes, with their associated fishes, dwindled, and now some of the pupfish only survive in minute environments. The Devil's Hole pupfish (*Cyprinodon diabolis*) lives only in a pool 10 × 50ft (3 × 15m) located 60ft (18m) below the desert floor in southern Nevada. It depends for food on the invertebrates living in the algae on a rock shelf 10 × 20ft (3 × 6m) just below the surface of the water. Although in a protected area in the Death Valley National Monument, distant pumping of subterranean water lowered the water table, threatening to expose the shelf and deprive the fish of its only source of food. Attempts to transplant some of the fish to other localities failed. Hastily a lower, artificial shelf was installed and the case was brought up before the US Supreme Court. They ruled in favor of the fish, the pumping was stopped, the water level stabilized and the Devil's Hole pupfish was saved.

The examples given above illustrate what is happening and what can be done. All the fishes mentioned live in fresh waters, where the area occupied is small enough for low-level population changes to be monitored. The same detailed knowledge about marine fishes is lacking because they can occupy much greater territories, precluding the col-

lection of such information.

For whatever reason, far too many species of fish are endangered, ie in danger of extinction. What is being done to secure their future? Many countries are signatories to an organization whose acronym is CITES (Convention on International Trade in Endangered Species). For this the member countries produce lists of their endangered animals and plants and all agree that there shall be no unlicenced trade in certain of the species. Unfortunately as there is little general awareness about fish, and hence little political capital to be gained, fish do not feature strongly on the CITES lists. Mammals and birds occupy the great majority of the pages. To complicate the issue, would a customs officer (who is largely responsible for the implementation of the rules by ascertaining that the species in the consignment are what they purport to be) be able to identify accurately the 5,000 species he might be confronted with? Even if he did (and many a professional fish specialist finds living fish difficult as the diagnostic characters may be internal) what would then happen to the fish? Even if it were possible to ship them back to their native land before they died, there is no guarantee they would be released into their original habitat.

Some countries follow the spirit of the laws of conservation better than others. In America, dam construction on the Colorado River prevented many of the endemic species from breeding. Many species quickly became very rare and were in danger of extinction. After prompting from scientists, the Dexter National Fish Hatchery was constructed in New Mexico and the endangered species were taken there and allowed to breed. The breeding program has been successful and many young are put back into suitable sites each year. But even this venture is only a partial answer. Pity poor *Gambusia amistadensis* that now lives and breeds in a reed-fringed pool at Dexter. It cannot be reintroduced. The Goodenough Spring, in which it lived, is now at the bottom of a reservoir.

A cynic might ask "Why bother to save a small fish from extinction?" There are two types of answer. The altruistic one is "because they are there and have as much right to be there as we have." The selfish answer is "because they could be of use to us." Living in a cave in Oman is a small, eyeless fish whose total population is probably 1,000. Recently it has been discovered that it can regrow about one-third of its brain (the optic lobes)—the only vertebrate known to do so. Such a discovery could be of great importance in human neuro-surgery. Luckily this fish was discovered; how many more useful attributes were there in fishes that have been allowed to die out?

The status of some species is more critical than others, but what happens to them all is almost entirely our decision. If the endangered species are to survive, the right decision must be taken—soon.

The Future of Fish

For a few years prior to 1882 there was an extensive fishery for a tile fish (*Lopholatilus chamaelionticeps*) off the east coast of America. This nutritious, tasty species reached about 3ft (90cm) in length and 40lb (18kg) in weight. Tile fishes lived in warm water near the edge of the continental shelf from 300 to 900ft (90–275m) down. During March and April 1882 millions and millions were found floating, dead, on the surface. One steamer reported voyaging for two days during which time it was never out of sight of tile fish corpses. For over 20 years no more were caught, but by 1915 the numbers had recovered enough to sustain a small fishery.

Despite the long gap in records, enough individuals must have survived to be able to rebuild the population, albeit to a lower level. The cause of this carnage is uncertain, but it is believed that ocean currents changed and the warm water in which the tile fish lived was rapidly replaced by an upwelling of deep, cold water in which they died.

Although many fish species undergo natural variations in abundance, for no matter what reason, a major natural disaster can affect them all. Should the population be at a low level at such a time, the chance of extinction, and the loss of a resource, could occur. Luckily the tile fish population was high when the currents changed.

It is largely axiomatic that where industries are few, rivers are clean. This is certainly true of parts of Scotland at least, where communities depend for financial viability on the spawning runs of the Atlantic salmon. For over a century the mainstay of the tourist/hotel business has been the anglers who stay in the hope of hooking a salmon. Nearer the coast are the netsmen who catch salmon as they begin their upstream migration and sell their luxury food in the markets further south. These communities remained stable and thrived, until an accidental observation was made in the late 1950s.

Before that time nobody knew where the

Herrings and History

Factors, both natural and unnatural, can combine on the most abundant species to produce the most alarming and unforeseen consequences. The Hanseatic states on the south coast of the Baltic prospered until the 15th century, because not only did they have a remarkably rich supply of herring on their doorsteps but they also knew how to preserve them and export them all over Europe. Then the herring suddenly left the Baltic for the North Sea. The Hanseatic states collapsed economically and politically and the Dutch rejoiced because they now had access to the herring. The Dutch had a good fleet and set about catching herring, frequently in British waters. Charles I of England decided that a good way of boosting his exchequer would be to tax the Dutch for fishing in his waters. To enforce the payment of this somewhat unwelcome tax and to keep British herring for the British, Charles had to build up the declining British Navy. The Dutch decided to protect their fishing boats and before too long the two countries were at war. Although that particular series of skirmishes was finally resolved, the dispute over the ownership of herrings (among others) continues. The most recent wrangle over herring quotas within the member states of the EEC is merely the modern, politely political equivalent of firing cannon balls at one another.

Parenthetically, one should note that "the battle of herrings" occurred in 1429 when Sir John Fastolf routed the French who tried to prevent him taking herrings to the Duke of Suffolk who was besieging Orleans.   KEB

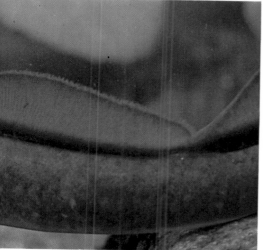

▲ **The sucking mouth** of lampreys is ringed by horny teeth which rasp away the flesh of their prey.

◄ **At rest, a Brook lamprey** lying near the bed of a stream. The row of seven gill openings, an eye and the nostril led to lampreys once being known as "nine-eyes." Young Brook lampreys, unlike those of other species, do not migrate to sea but move straight to the spawning area where spawning begins immediately.

Europe the Brook lamprey begins its run in September or October but in the Adriatic region the peak comes in February and March. In northwest Russia there are spring and fall runs. Lampreys in the southern hemisphere spend much longer on the spawning run and may not spawn until a year or more after they enter fresh water. The spawning grounds may be several hundred miles from the estuary and lampreys may, in slow-flowing stretches, be able to travel at 2mi (about 3km) each day. Weirs and rapids may be overcome, and lampreys cope with weariness by temporarily holding on to rocks with their suckers. Lampreys do not feed during the spawning run.

During the upstream migration and the subsequent spawning some changes in body shape occur. These may be as minor as the changes in the relative positions of the two dorsal fins and the anal fin or as substantial as the enlargement of the disk (sucker) in males of the southern genera *Geotria* and *Mordacia*. The males of *Geotria australis* and *Mordacia lapicida* (but not of other species of *Mordacia*) develop a large, spectacular, sac-like extension of the throat. Its function is unknown.

The spawning grounds, often used year after year, are chosen for particular characteristics of which gravel of the right size for the larvae to live in seems to be the most important. Other features are less important, although water about 3ft (1m) deep and of moderate current is favored. The males of the Sea lamprey arrive first and start building a nest by moving stones around to make an oval, shallow depression with a gravelly bottom. Large stones are removed and the rest graded, with the biggest upstream. All species of lamprey build similar nests but in different species the sex of the nest-builder differs and may not be consistent.

Spawning is usually a group activity, in groups of 10–30 in the Brook lamprey, in small numbers in the Sea lamprey, often a pair to a nest. In the Freshwater lamprey there is courtship. While the male is building the nest the female swims overhead and passes the posterior part of her body close to the male's head. It is suggested that stimulation by smell may be involved. Fertilization occurs externally, the male and female twining together and shedding sperm and eggs, respectively, into the water. Using her sucker the female attaches herself to a stone and the male then sucks onto her to remain in position during spawning. In the Brook lamprey two or three males may attach to the same female. Only a few eggs are extruded at a time, so mating takes place at frequent intervals over several days. The eggs are sticky and adhere to the sand grains, and the continued spawning activity of the adults covers the eggs with more sand. After spawning the adults die.

The eggs hatch into burrowing larvae (called ammocoetes) which are structurally unlike the adults. Their eyes are small and hidden beneath the skin, and light is detected by a photosensitive region near the tail. The sucking mouth with its horny teeth is not yet developed. Instead there is an oral hood, rather like a cowl or a greatly expanded upper lip, at the base of which is the mouth surrounded by a ring of filaments

(cirri) which act as strainers. Water is drawn through the oral hood by the action of the gill pouches and of a valve-like structure behind the mouth called the velum. On the inner surface of the hood are rows of minute hairs (cilia) and much sticky mucus. Particles in the water are caught on the mucus and the action of the cilia channels the food-rich mucus through the mouth into a complex glandular duct (the endostyle) at the base of the pharynx. The ability of the ammocoetes to secrete mucus is important, for not merely does it enable them to feed but it also helps them to cement the walls of their burrows and stop them from collapsing.

Ammocoetes rarely leave their burrows, and then only at night, but they frequently change position. In the burrows they lie partially on their backs, tail down, with oral hood facing into the current. In this position the importance of the photosensitive tail region can now be appreciated: it helps the ammocoete to orient itself correctly. The longest phase in the life history of lampreys is spent as ammocoete larvae (often called "prides"). The Sea lamprey can pass seven years of its life in this stage, *Ichthyomyzon fossor* six, the Brook lamprey three to six years and *Mordacia mordax* three years.

Although lampreys live successfully as ammocoetes and as adults, the change from one state to the other is a dangerous period, from which high mortality results. The changes involved are profound: the entire mouth and the feeding and digestive systems have to be restructured, eyes have to be developed and the burrowing habit abandoned for a free-swimming one. During this time, which may last for eight months, lampreys do not and cannot feed. It was discovered in Russia, for example, that large numbers of metamorphosing lampreys found dead during early spring had been

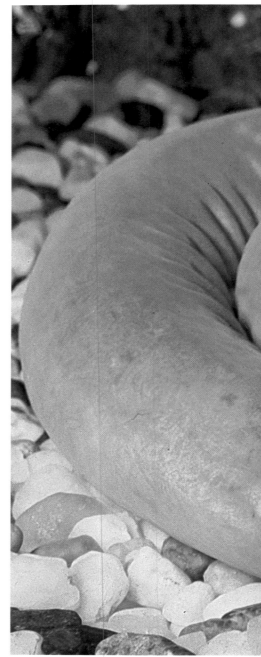

◄ **Anchored against the flow,** a Brook lamprey uses its sucker to hold itself fast to a rock. The lamprey mouth is efficient and effective, being used for carrying stones for the nest and in mating.

▼ **Hagfish are normally sedentary,** living in burrows in mud, the walls of which are partly reinforced by secretions of slime. Hagfish eat rarely; they have a low metabolic rate and store a lot of fat. When they are hungry their sedentary habits cease. They swim around leisurely, tasting odors in the water by lifting their heads and spreading their barbels.

effectively suffocated by the breakdown of the velum, after the skin of the gills and the mouth had been blocked by mucus.

Metamorphosis in northern hemisphere lampreys usually starts in late summer. In any given area the ammocoetes start their transformation almost simultaneously, mostly within a couple of weeks. Environmental conditions seem to be the trigger: it has been noted that the metamorphosis starts earlier in colder waters. Initially the newly eyed adults are inactive but then a downstream migration begins. It is now that the difference between the parasitic and nonparasitic lampreys becomes important. After metamorphosis nonparasitic lampreys

do not feed: they breed and die. Hence all their growth is spent as a larva. Parasitic lampreys, however, feed on the blood and fluids of fishes for up to two years, sometimes with spectacular effect.

During the parasitic phase lampreys travel extensively. Species that go to sea have been caught many miles off the coast and at depths as great as 3,300ft (about 1000m). Lampreys detect their prey by sight and usually attach to the lower side surface in the central third of the body. They move in with the sucker closed to reduce water resistance, but open it just before attack. After attachment they may move to a more favorable position. The opening of the disk brings the teeth into play. Only rarely do fish free themselves of lampreys, by coming to the surface and turning over so that the lamprey's head is in the air. During the course of the parasitic phase it has been calculated that 3lb (1.4kg) of fish blood will suffice to feed the lamprey from metamorphosis to spawning. Scarcely any fish is immune from attack, not even the garfishes which are covered with diamond-shaped scutes. Several lampreys may attack the same fish and newly metamorphosed individuals are the most voracious.

Any change in the environment may have unforeseen circumstances. There used to be an extensive and profitable fishery for trout in the Great Lakes of North America. When the Welland Canal was built to allow ships to sail from Lake Ontario into Lake Erie (opened in 1828) it also let through sea lampreys. From Lake Erie they traveled into lakes Huron, Michigan and Superior. By the mid 1950s sea lampreys were well established and the fishery was decimated. Considerable attempts were made to control the lampreys and restock the trout, but not only were these attempts expensive, they were also unsuccessful. The only real hope now is that a biological balance will be achieved before pollution wipes out all the fish life.

Hagfishes are superficially undistinguished and unprepossessing animals. They are eel-like, white to pale brown, with a fleshy median fin on the flattened caudal region and four or six tentacles around the mouth. But their superficial simplicity hides a number of extraordinary, even unique, features. Hagfishes have neither jaws nor stomach, yet they are parasites of larger fishes. They have few predators but defend themselves by exuding large amounts of slime. They can tie their bodies into knots. They also have several sets of hearts.

There are 32 species, which rarely exceed

28in (about 70cm) in length and live in cold oceanic waters at depths from 65 to 1,000ft (20 to about 300m). The exact number of species is not known for certain because of the paucity of agreed, tangible characters and the unknown degree of individual variability. (The two best known genera are *Eptatretus* and *Myxine*.) The relationship of the hagfishes to the other extant jawless fishes, the lampreys, is uncertain and the subject of much debate.

The mouth is surrounded by four or six tentacles according to species. There are no eyes; instead there are two pigmented depressions on the head and other, unpigmented, regions on the head and around the cloaca that can detect the presence of light. The senses of touch and smell are well developed. There is a single median nostril above the mouth which leads into the pharynx; a blind olfactory sac is also present which detects odors. During breathing, water enters the nostril from where it is pumped by the velum to the 14 or so pairs of gill pouches leading from the pharynx to the outside. In the gill pouches oxygen is taken from the water by the blood which simultaneously loses its carbon dioxide. It is thought that the skin also absorbs oxygen and excretes carbon dioxide. Externally the gill pouches are visible as a series of small pores, increasing in size towards the rear. This row is continued by small openings of the slime glands. The only teeth of the hagfish are on the tongue.

The main prey of hagfishes are dying or dead fish and when these are detected the hagfishes swim rapidly upcurrent to reach them. Now the tongue and flexible body come into play. The toothed tongue quickly rasps a hole in the side of the fish. With a large fish extra leverage is needed, so hagfishes loop their bodies into a half hitch and use the fore part of this loop as a fulcrum to help thrust the head into the body of the fish. Hagfishes feed quickly and may soon be completely inside the fish, voraciously eating the flesh. It is not rare for a trawler to catch the remains of a fish almost hollow save for a sated hagfish inside. Worms and other invertebrates are also eaten.

The ability to knot the body has other uses. It can be used to evade capture, especially when this is coupled with slime secretion. Knotting is also used to clear a hagfish of secreted slime which might otherwise clog gill openings and cause suffocation. In this case it simply wipes itself free of slime by sliding through the knot. The nostril cannot be cleared in this maneuver, so a powerful "sneeze" has been developed to

reestablish normal nasal functions. Slime is secreted into water as cotton-like cells which, on contact with sea water, rapidly expand, coagulate and form a tenacious mucous covering. A single North Atlantic hagfish (*Myxine glutinosa*) 18in (45cm) long can, when placed in a bucket of sea water, turn the entire contents of the bucket into slime.

Like most fish hagfishes have a heart to pump the blood through the fine vessels of the gills. However, they also have a pair of hearts to speed the blood after it has passed through the gills. Another heart pumps the blood into the liver, and there is a pair of small hearts, like reciprocating pumps, near the tail. These accessory hearts are necessary because in hagfishes alone the blood is not always contained in restraining blood vessels. Hagfish have a series of open spaces or "blood-lakes," called sinuses, in which there is a great drop in blood pressure. An accessory heart is found after each sinus to increase the pressure and push the blood on to the next part of the circulatory system. The tail hearts are a puzzle. They are

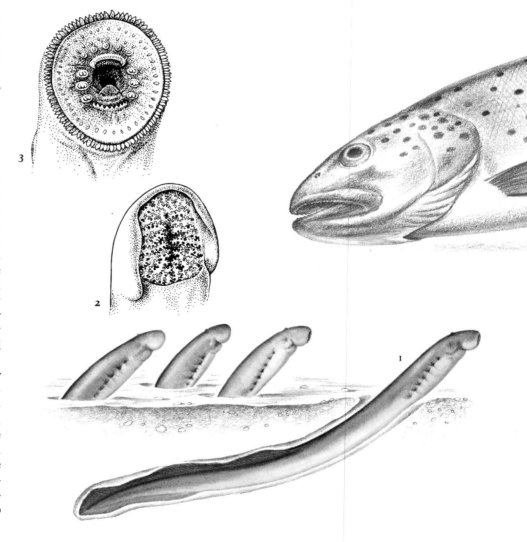

▼ ► **Lampreys and hagfishes.** (1) Juvenile lampreys (ammocoete larvae) on the bottom, filtering detritus from water (3–4in, 8–10cm). (2) Head of a juvenile Freshwater lamprey (*Lampetra fluviatilis*) showing the oral hood. (3) Mouth of an adult Freshwater lamprey showing horny teeth. (4) River lampreys feeding of a sea trout (20–24in, 50–60cm). (5) A Sea lamprey building a nest (1m, 3.3ft). (6) Head of a hagfish (a species of the genus *Myxine*) showing the mouth and nostril surrounded by tentacles. (7) A hagfish of the genus *Myxine*, showing its eel-like form (24in, 60cm). (8) A hagfish about to enter the body of its prey. By twisting into a knot it can gain extra leverage for thrusting itself into the fish.

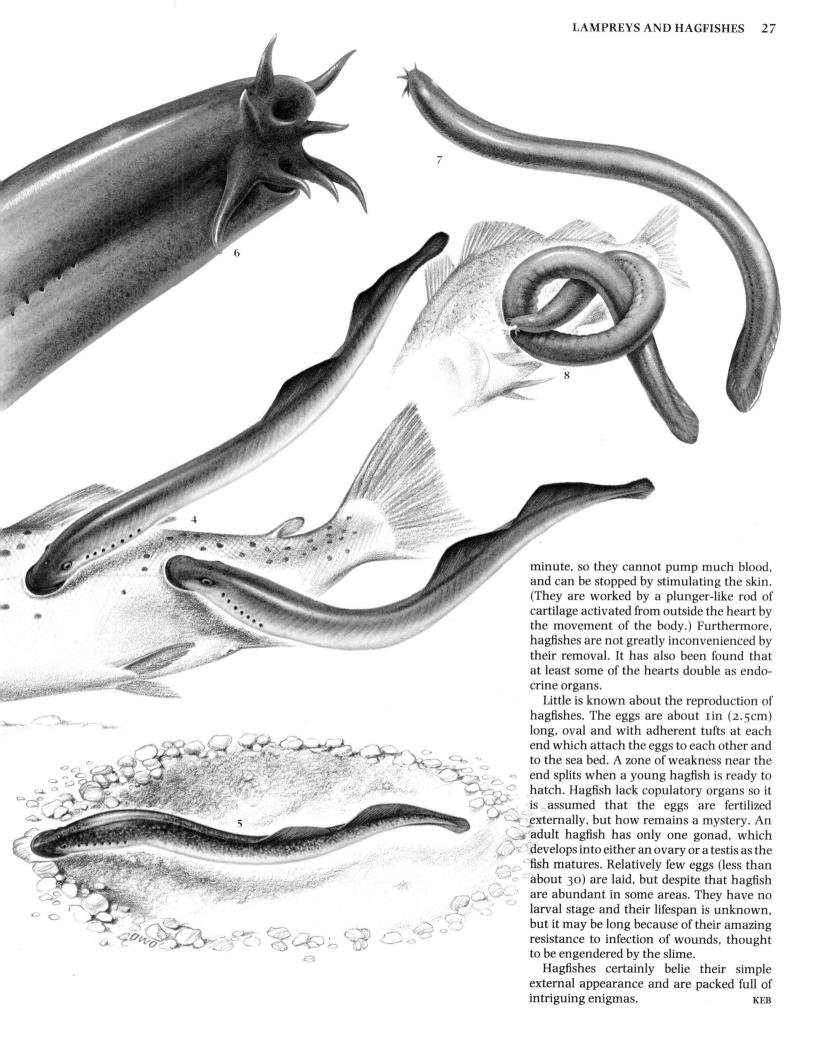

minute, so they cannot pump much blood, and can be stopped by stimulating the skin. (They are worked by a plunger-like rod of cartilage activated from outside the heart by the movement of the body.) Furthermore, hagfishes are not greatly inconvenienced by their removal. It has also been found that at least some of the hearts double as endocrine organs.

Little is known about the reproduction of hagfishes. The eggs are about 1in (2.5cm) long, oval and with adherent tufts at each end which attach the eggs to each other and to the sea bed. A zone of weakness near the end splits when a young hagfish is ready to hatch. Hagfish lack copulatory organs so it is assumed that the eggs are fertilized externally, but how remains a mystery. An adult hagfish has only one gonad, which develops into either an ovary or a testis as the fish matures. Relatively few eggs (less than about 30) are laid, but despite that hagfish are abundant in some areas. They have no larval stage and their lifespan is unknown, but it may be long because of their amazing resistance to infection of wounds, thought to be engendered by the slime.

Hagfishes certainly belie their simple external appearance and are packed full of intriguing enigmas. KEB

STURGEONS, PADDLEFISHES

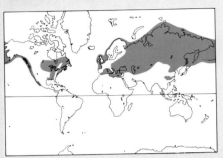

Order: Acipenseriformes
Twenty-seven species in 6 genera and
2 families.

Sturgeons
Family: Acipenseridae
Twenty-five species in 4 genera.
Distribution: North Atlantic, North Pacific and
Arctic oceans and associated feeder rivers.
Size: adult length 3–20ft (0.9–6m)
Species include: **Baltic sturgeon** (*Acipenser
sturio*), **beluga** (*Huso huso*), **Kaluga sturgeon**
(*H. dauricus*), **Lake sturgeon** (*Acipenser
fulvescens*), **sterlet** (*A. ruthenus*), **White sturgeon**
(*A. transmontanus*).

Paddlefishes
Family: Polyodontidae
Two species in 2 genera.
Distribution: Mississippi and Yangtze rivers.
Size: maximum adult length about 10ft (3m).
Species: **Chinese paddlefish** (*Psephurus gladius*),
paddlefish (*Polyodon spathula*).

STURGEONS are amazing. They are the largest freshwater fishes, and the longest lived. They also provide the expensive delicacy caviar.

Sturgeons and paddlefishes are the only survivors of an ancient group of fishes known from the Upper Cretaceous period (135–100 million years ago). (Together with five extinct orders they form the infraclass Chondrostei.) Today they are confined to the northern hemisphere, within which there are two distributions, one centered on the Pacific, the other on the Atlantic.

Sturgeons have heavy, almost cylindrical bodies which bear rows of large ivory-like nodules in the skin (scutes or bucklers), a ventral mouth surrounded by barbels, a heterocercal tail and a cartilaginous skeleton.

Some sturgeons live in the sea but breed in fresh water, others live entirely in fresh water. Little is known of the life at sea of anadromous sturgeons. They appear to take a wide variety of food including mollusks, polychaete worms, shrimps and fishes. Adults have few enemies, though they are known to be attacked and even killed by the sea lamprey. The Baltic sturgeon has been found at depths of over 330ft (100m) in submarine canyons off the continental shelf. Although it was known that the Kaluga sturgeon inhabited fishing grounds off Sakhalin Island (USSR), it was not until 1975 that the first specimens were caught in the well-fished grounds off Hokkaido, northern Japan. The White sturgeon is known to travel over 625mi (1,000km) during its time at sea. Freshwater sturgeons usually remain in shoal areas of large lakes and rivers feeding on crayfish, mollusks, insect larvae and various other invertebrates, but rarely on fishes. Seasonal movements are from shallow to deeper waters in the summer and a return to the shallows in winter. In the Volga sturgeons overwinter along a 270mi (430km) stretch, aggregating in bottom depressions.

Anadromous sturgeons spawn during spring and summer months, though in some species there are "spring" and "winter" forms which ascend the rivers in their respective seasons. The spring form spawns soon after going up the river whereas the winter form spawns the following spring. Some adults spawn every year, others intermittently. Freshwater sturgeons make their way from their home streams and lakes into the upper or middle reaches of large rivers. The North American Lake sturgeon will spawn over rocks in wave conditions when more suitable quiet areas are unavailable. Courtship involves the fish leaping and rolling near the bottom.

Both anadromous and freshwater species cease feeding during the spawning period. Eggs (caviar) are produced in millions— over 3 million in a female Atlantic sturgeon 8.7ft (2.65m) long. They are adhesive, attaching to vegetation and stones. Hatching takes about a week. Few data are available on the development of the young but growth is generally rapid in the first five years, approximately 20in (50cm).

The size and age of sturgeons are impressive; the White sturgeon of North America and the Russian beluga are the world's largest freshwater fishes. An 1,800lb (800kg) White sturgeon caught in Oregon in 1892 was exhibited at the Chicago World Fair, but the only great White sturgeon actually weighed and measured came from the Columbia River (Canada and USA). Caught in 1912, it was 12.5ft (3.8m) long and weighed 1,285lb (580kg), When 6ft (1.8m) long the White sturgeon is between 15 and 20 years old. The largest Lake sturgeon, caught in 1922, weighed in at 310lb (140kg), and the greatest recorded age was 154 years for a specimen caught in 1953. A beluga caught in 1926 weighed over 2,200lb (1,000kg) and yielded 396lb (180kg) of caviar and 1,500lb (688kg) of flesh; it was at least 75 years old.

▲ **An indoor sturgeon.** The sterlet has recently proved to be a popular though expensive aquarium fish. It is an attractive animal, but not easy to feed. It favors finely ground mussels, but unless great care is taken it will not live long.

◄ **Eating apparatus.** The paddlefish is a filter-feeder, that is it sieves food out of the water using gill rakers, which are prominent in this picture. The long rostrum may enable the fish to detect the zooplankton on which it feeds.

▼ **Treasure from a frozen wilderness**—fishing for sturgeon in Siberia c. 1870. Today caviar (sturgeon eggs or roe) is one of the USSR's most famous exports.

There are two **paddlefishes**, the American paddlefish of the Mississippi and the Chinese paddlefish of the Yangtze, but fossils are known from North America from the Cretaceous and Eocene periods (135–38 million years ago).

Paddlefishes are instantly recognized from their long, flat broad snout. The mouth is sack-like and the gapes open as the fish swims, scooping up crustaceans and other plankton. The American paddlefish occurs in silty reservoirs and rivers; in length it exceeds 5ft (1.5m) and weighs up to 175lb (80kg). The fish is nocturnal, resting at the bottom of deep pools during the day. Spawning was first observed only in 1961. When

water temperature reaches 50°F (10°C) adults are stimulated to move upstream to shallows.

The function of the paddle-like upper jaw is uncertain. It is suggested that it is an electrical sensory device for detecting plankton swarms; a stabilizer to balance the head against downward pressure in the huge mouth; a scoop; a mud-digger; or even a beater to release small organisms from aquatic plants (though individuals that lost their paddles in accidents are known to feed perfectly, from the evidence of their full stomachs).

Virtually nothing is known of the biology of the Chinese paddlefish. GJH

Sturgeons and Man

To Longfellow's Hiawatha (1855) the Lake sturgeon was "Mishe-Nahma, King of Fishes"; on the early explorers of North America the mighty fish also made a deep impression: witness the numbers of Sturgeon rivers, Sturgeon bays, lakes, falls etc on the map of North America. To ancient man in both America and Russia sturgeons were a valuable resource. Scutes were used as scrapers, oils as medicine, flesh as food, eggs, latterly, as a caviar. Horrendously, steamboats in North America could trawl large numbers of sturgeons and used their oil as fuel, thereby speeding their demise. Thousands more were butchered by 1885—when over 5 million lb (2 million kg) of smoked sturgeon were sold at Sandusky, Ohio, and distributed to cities.

The eggs or roe provide the sturgeon's most prized product: caviar. The center of the caviar trade is the Russian Caspian Sea basin. Here sturgeons were fished intensively for 200 years, and by 1900 stocks had declined dramatically. The First World War and

internal strife allowed some recovery of stock but by 1930 feeding grounds were intensively overfished and dam construction depleted the fishery even more by precluding breeding migrations. The development of sturgeon hatcheries in the 1950s conserved and increased populations; the hatcheries released millions of young (45 million in 1965) into the rivers. Fishing for sturgeon is now banned in the USSR. A product which also led to a reduction in sturgeon stocks was isinglass.

Procured from the sturgeon's swim bladder and vertebrae it was used as a clarifier of wines and a gelatinizing agent for jams and jellies. In 1885 about 3,000lb (1,350kg) of isinglass were exported (derived from approximately 30,000 sturgeons).

Today in both the USSR and the USA the plight of the sturgeon is recognized. However, with few biological data and constant modification of the environment the situation of many species is precarious.

BOWFIN, GARFISHES

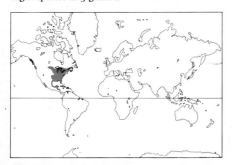

Families: Amiidae, Lepisosteidae
Eight species in 3 genera.

Bowfin
Family: Amiidae
Sole species *Amia calva*.
Distribution: N America from the Great Lakes
S to Florida and the Mississippi Valley.
Size: length 18–39in (45–100cm), maximum
weight 9lb (4kg).

Garfishes
Family: Lepisosteidae
Seven species in 2 genera.
Distribution: C America, Cuba, N America as
far N as the Great Lakes.
Size: length 2.5–13ft (75cm–4m), weight
15–62lb (7–28kg).
Species: **Alligator gar** (*Atractosteus spatula*),
Cuban gar (*A. tristoechus*), **Florida spotted gar**
(*Lepisosteus oculatus*), **Longnose gar** (*L. osseus*),
Shortnose gar (*L. platostomus*), **Spotted gar**
(*L. platyrhincus*).

THE **bowfin** is a renowned fish, its fame being due to its size, predatory habits, ability to survive out of water and its status as the only living representative of a group of primitive bony fishes (the Halecomorphi) whose ancestral lineage stretches back to the Jurassic period (195–135 million years ago). Its systematic position, however, has been contentious for many years, and among bony fishes its anatomy is probably the most thoroughly described. The cranial anatomy alone forms the subject of a 300-page monograph (by Edward Allis) published in 1897. (Present opinion is that bowfins are most closely related to the Teleostei.)

During the Tertiary period (65–7 million years ago) bowfins were widely distributed in Eurasia and North America. Nowadays only one species survives, in central and eastern North America.

The common name alludes to the bowfin's long, undulating dorsal fin. In the Great Lakes it is known as the dog-fish, and in the southern states as the grindle. The other distinctive features of the bowfin are its massive blunt head and cylindrical body. At the upper base of the tail is a dark spot, edged in orange or yellow in males (probably a sign for recognition). Females lack the edging and sometimes the spot itself. Most bowfins grow to 18–24in (45–60cm) long but a few will reach 3.3ft (1m) and weigh 9lb (4kg).

Bowfins can use their air bladder as a "lung" and can survive a day out of water. This feature enables them to exist in swampy, stagnant waters unusable by other predatory fish. There is also evidence that during dry conditions individuals enter a state of torpor (aestivate). Bowfins spawn in spring; males move to shallow water and each prepares a saucer-shaped nest, 12–24in (30–60cm) across, by biting away plants growing in the bed of the river or lake. The males vigorously defend their nesting sites against other males but often spawn

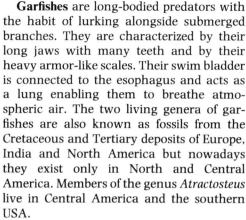

Garfishes are long-bodied predators with the habit of lurking alongside submerged branches. They are characterized by their long jaws with many teeth and by their heavy armor-like scales. Their swim bladder is connected to the esophagus and acts as a lung enabling them to breathe atmospheric air. The two living genera of garfishes are also known as fossils from the Cretaceous and Tertiary deposits of Europe, India and North America but nowadays they exist only in North and Central America. Members of the genus *Atractosteus* live in Central America and the southern USA.

The Alligator gar is one of the largest North American freshwater fishes. One weighing over 300lb (135kg) and 10ft (3m) long was caught in Louisiana. It is now scarce throughout its range (an arc along the Gulf coast plain from Veracruz to the Ohio and Missouri rivers). It has been "accused" of eating game fishes and waterfowl. However, careful studies have shown that the Alligator gar rarely feeds on these animals and preys mostly on forage fishes and crabs. The other two *Atractosteus* species are *A. tropicus* of Nicaragua and the Cuban gar. Little is known of their biology; *A. tropicus* inhabits the shallow, protected areas of Lake Nicaragua, where specimens can grow to over 3.6ft (1.1m) and weigh over 20lb (9kg).

▲ **The long dorsal fin,** to which the bowfin's name alludes, allows it to remain stationary while it watches for prey. It catches its food by surging forward, fast acceleration being provided by the powerful sweeps of its muscular body.

◄ **This alligator-like snout** and the heavily enameled diamond-shaped ganoid scales are those of the Cuban gar. The speckled color pattern is part of the camouflage of this lurking predator.

▼ **Sleek and sleepy,** a garfish of the genus *Atractosteus*. Its three extant species are restricted to northern America; fossil species are also known from Europe and India.

with several females. Females lay about 30,000 adhesive eggs, which the male guards and fans. In 8–10 days the eggs hatch and the young fish cling to vegetation by an adhesive snout pad. The male continues to guard the brood until the young are about 4in (10cm) long.

Bowfins are predators; they feed mostly on other fish (sunfish, bass, perch, pike, catfish and minnows), frogs, crayfish, shrimps and various water insects. Bowfin flesh itself is unsavory, and its plundering of sport fishes and comparative abundance make for few friends amongst fishermen and conservationists.

The genus *Lepisosteus* has a wider distribution, from the northern Great Lakes to Florida and the Mississippi basin. The Spotted gar occurs throughout the Mississippi drainage and grows to over 3.6ft (1.1m) and a weight of 6.6lb (3kg). The distribution of the Longnose gar is wider than that of the Spotted gar, and it too inhabits brackish water in its coastal range. The Longnose gar can grow to over 5.9ft (1.8m) and weigh 66lb (30kg). The females are longer than the males, the difference being as much as 7in (18cm) in their tenth or eleventh year. Males rarely survive beyond this period, but females may live for up to 22 years. Group spawning occurs from March to August, according to locality, in shallow warm water over vegetation. The adhesive eggs, about 27,000 per female, are scattered randomly and hatch within 6–8 days. As in the bowfin the young cling to vegetation by means of an adhesive pad on their snout. Growth is rapid, 0.1–0.15in (2.5–3.9mm) per day. The Shortnose gar covers an area embracing northeastern Texas, Montana, southern Ohio and the Mississippi, whilst the Florida spotted gar occurs there and in the lowlands of Georgia.   GJH

TARPONS, EELS, NOTACANTHS

Superorder: Elopomorpha
About six hundred and thirty-two species in
about 160 genera and about 30 families.

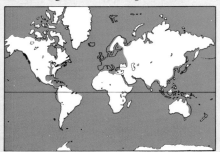

Tarpons and allies
Order: Elopiformes
About twelve species in 4 genera and
3 families.
Distribution: most tropical seas. Rarely
brackish or fresh water.
Size: maximum length about 6.5ft (2m),
maximum weight 350lb (160kg).
Species include: **Bone fish** (*Albula vulpes*),
Pacific tarpon (*Megalops cyprinoides*), **tarpon**
(*Tarpon atlanticus*), **tenpounder** (*Elops saurus*).

Eels
Order: Anguilliformes
About six hundred species in about 150 genera
and 24 families.
Distribution: all oceans, N America, Europe,
E Africa, Madagascar, S India, Sri Lanka,
SE Asia, Malay Archipelago, N and E Australia,
New Zealand.
Size: maximum length about 10ft (3m).
Families, genera and species include: **anguillid
eels** (family Anguillidae), including **American
eel** (*Anguilla rostrata*), **European eel** (*A. anguilla*),
Japanese eel (*A. japonica*); **curtailed snipe eels**
(family Cyemidae); **garden eels** (family
Heterocongridae); **Gulper eel** (family
Eurypharyngidae, sole species *Eurypharynx
pelecanoides*); **monognathids** (family
Monognathidae); **moray eels** (family
Muraenidae), including **moray eels** (genus
Muraena); **saccopharyngids** (family
Saccopharyngidae); **snipe eels** (family
Nemichthyidae); **Snub-nosed parasitic eel**
(family Simenchelyidae, sole species
Simenchelys parasiticus); **synaphobranchid eels**
(family Synaphobranchidae); **worm** or **spaghetti
eels** (family Moringuidae); **xenocongrid eels**
(family Xenocongridae).

Notacanths
Order Notacanthiformes
About twenty species in 6 genera and
3 families.
Distribution: all oceans.
Size: maximum length about 6.5ft (2m).
Families include: **halosaurs** (Halosauridae),
notacanthids (Notacanthidae).

▶ **Scaling a tarpon** in Northeast Brazil. The
Atlantic tarpon is a large and prized food fish.
Its scales have been incorporated into jewelry.

▶ **A shoal of tarpon** OPPOSITE, feeding around
a rocky outcrop.

EELS have long been prized and in the
Middle Ages were a staple food. But it
was then believed that eels were different:
unlike other freshwater fish they did not
produce eggs and sperm at the start of the
breeding season. Where did eels come from?
The problem produced ingenious answers
but no solution until the end of the 19th
century. Even today eel behavior retains
many mysteries.

The superorder of tarpons, eels and notacanths comprises three orders, the members
of each of which seem to be unlike the
others, apart from certain anatomical
similarities. They are united in having a
larva that is quite unlike the adult: it is
transparent, the shape of a willow leaf or rib-
bon and is graced with the name of leptocephalus. The three orders are the
Elopiformes, containing the tarpons,
tenpounder and the Bone fish; the Anguilliformes with about 24 families of eels; and
the Notacanthiformes which lack any
accepted common name—sometimes they
are called deep sea spiny eels, but as this is
abbreviated to "spiny eels" they could be
confused with the unrelated family that
aquarists call "spiny eels"; confusion will be
avoided by using the name "notacanths."

The un-eel-like **tarpons** and allies represent an ancient lineage. Fossils belonging to
this group occur in the Upper Cretaceous
deposits of Europe, Asia and Africa (135–
100 million years ago). In addition to
developing from a leptocephalus larva they
all possess gular plates—a pair of superficial
bones in the skin of the throat between each
side of the lower jaw. Gular plates were
much more common in ancient fishes than
they are in living fishes. All are marine fish.

The tarpon is the largest fish in the group,
weighing up to 350lb (160kg). It is a
popular angling fish because it gives the
angler a fight, leaping into the air, twisting
and turning to dislodge the hook. This species lives in the tropical waters on both sides
of the Atlantic: the adults breed at sea and
the larvae make their way inshore where
they metamorphose. The young live and
grow in lagoons and mangrove swamps.
These swampy regions can often be low in
oxygen, but the tarpon can breathe atmospheric oxygen and does so at such times.

The Pacific tarpon is very similar in
appearance and even has the last ray of the
dorsal fin similarly prolonged. Its life cycle
is also like that of the tarpon. Apart from
some minor anatomical differences (in the
way that processes from the swim bladder
come to lie closely against the region of the
inner ear in the skull) the most obvious difference is that the Pacific tarpon is smaller,
rarely reaching 110lb (50kg).

The tenpounder is another warm-water
species, known from the tropical Atlantic.
What may be a different species is widespread in the Indo-Pacific. Despite its common name it can reach 15lb (6.8kg) in
weight.

The Bone fish is widespread in shallow
tropical marine waters. It is a shoaling fish
and feeds on bottom-living invertebrates,
often in water so shallow that the dorsal fin
and upper lobe of the caudal fin stick out
of the water. Although rarely exceeding 20lb
(9kg) it is, despite its poor flavor, a much
sought after angling fish because of its fighting qualities.

The exact number of families of **eels** is
uncertain. There are differences of opinion
because some groups are poorly known—
sometimes on the basis of just one or a few
specimens. In addition there is the problem
of matching up the known leptocephali with
the known adults.

The larvae of European eels hatch in the
Sargasso Sea (see box) and then drift back
in the Gulf Stream and take about three
years to reach the colder, shallower and
fresher European coastal waters. Here they
shrink slightly, metamorphose into elvers
and move upstream, where they grow and
feed until some years later the urge to
migrate comes upon them. The American

The Colonies of Garden Eels

There are about twenty species of garden eels grouped into three genera, and it seems that the daily cycle and life histories of all are very similar. Colonies usually live in shallow water where there is sufficient light for the eels to see their food and a reasonable current. There the eels give a passable imitation of prehensile walking sticks facing into the current. The densest colonies are deepest, with perhaps one eel every 20in (50cm). The distance apart depends upon the length of the eel. Each eel occupies a hemisphere of water with a radius similar to the eel's body length, so that it is just separated from its neighbor.

A colony of *Gorgasia sillneri* in the Red Sea has been studied intensively and has produced some interesting information. The eels' burrows themselves are twisted and lined with mucus secreted by the skin (during the period of study, no eel ever left its burrow). The eels' day starts about half an hour before sunrise when they emerge. By sunrise all are out eating. Any disturbance causes the whole colony to disappear. For a period either side of noon the eels rest in their burrows, but from mid afternoon to sunset they are out feeding again. An interesting phenomenon is that while the eels are in their burrows their feeding space is taken over by another fish (*Trichonotus nikii*), which feeds at the level of where the eels' heads would be. When the eels are out the fish hides in the sand.

Even mating is conducted from the security of the burrow. The male stretches out and ripples his iridescent fins at the adjacent female. She stretches out of her burrow and they intertwine. A few eggs are shed and fertilized at a time and a couple may mate 20 times a day. Detailed study of a plot within a colony showed that females never moved their burrows but some males did, to be near females. As this movement was never observed it was presumed to take place at night. The males also moved away from the females after breeding.

Small eels settle down together until they are about 10in (25cm) long when the colony breaks up and the eels try to find a place in an adult colony. The adults resent this intrusion and unless the juvenile can stand up to aggression it moves away to a new area.

A major predator of garden eels is the ray. The effect of a ray swimming over a colony has been likened to a mower cutting grass. Whether the eels retreat in time or are caught has not been satisfactorily ascertained.

◄ **A congregation of eels.** The Conger eel (*Conger conger*) is an Atlantic species. Largely nocturnal, it hides away by day. Although it resembles the European and American anguillid eels it never enters fresh waters.

▲ **Dimorphic duo.** Some eels, such as these worm eels of the species *Moringua edwardsii*, show marked differences between the sexes. Here the size and nature of the fins are very different.

▼ **The mark of a family.** Synaphobranchid eels are sometimes called cut-throat eels: they have a single ventral gill-slit. They are found in most oceans and some are parasitic.

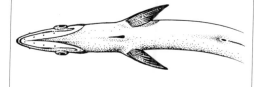

tail regions being used to penetrate the sand. Their distribution is similar to that of the worm eels.

Three further families of eels (Dysommatidae, Synaphobranchidae and Simenchelyidae) are here grouped together because the present division into three families may not be justified. All have leptocephali with an unusual characteristic: telescopic eyes. This may well indicate a very close relationship.

The genus *Dysomma* includes about six species characterized by enlarged teeth in the roof of the mouth (vomerine teeth). There is also a tendency towards the loss of the pectoral fin. The species tend to be laterally compressed and to taper evenly towards the tail. The swim bladder is very long and the nostrils are tubular. The main reason for including this otherwise unremarkable Indo-Pacific family is because of the history of the genus *Media* which exemplifies some of the problems faced by ichthyologists. A fish was bought in a fish market near Kochi in Japan. No one knew what it was and it became the type of the new species (and genus) *Media abyssalis*. During the Second World War this specimen was destroyed by fire. Not until 1950 were more caught off Japan and off Hawaii. Although the search for this brownish, scaleless eel was not particularly assiduous, it does show how fate can destroy, so easily, the only representatives available to the scientific world of a species that is probably common in its own particular habitat.

The thought of fire and the dysommatid eels brings us to fire and the synaphobranchid eels. Uncommon in collections, synaphobranchids are deep-sea eels with the gill slits almost confluent ventrally, giving them the vernacular name of cut-throat eels. In the course of one expedition a deep-sea research vessel, *Galathea*, caught 12 specimens. These were sent, in three separate parcels for safety, to a researcher in New Zealand. The second parcel, with five specimens, was destroyed in a fire in a mail-storage warehouse in Wellington in July 1961.

Cut-throat eels live in cold, deep waters, where temperatures average 41°F (5°C). They feed on crustaceans and fishes. (One specimen of *Synaphobranchus kaupi*, trawled at a depth of 3,300ft (1,000m), had eaten octopus eggs.) They are thick set, scaled eels with large jaws and small teeth. The scale pattern is like that of the following family. Several species have a characteristic nick in the ventral outline of the body just below the pectoral fin. The genus *Haptenchelys* is odd in lacking scales. Their distribution is

worldwide from 6,600 to 1,300ft (2,000–400m) deep. The adults are bottom dwellers, the larvae have telescopic eyes, but beyond that little is known about their life history.

The third family in this assemblage (Simenchelyidae) probably has just one species, the Snub-nosed parasitic eel, but as in many other instances there is no agreement on the matter. This deep-sea eel has been caught off the eastern coast of Canada, in the western and northern Pacific, off South Africa and off New Zealand. Whether these discrete collecting localities reflect different local species, or just the collecting effort, is impossible to say. It seems to be plentiful because it is caught in large numbers. It may be a gregarious species or it may need a particular habitat. It has a blunt head with a small transverse mouth. Jaws and jaw muscles are strong. The gill slits are short and lie horizontally below the pectoral fins. The dorsal fin starts well in advance of the anal fin. The body is cylindrical until the anus and compressed thereafter. The small scales are grouped and angled acutely to the lateral line.

The young eat small crustaceans but the adult is probably at least partly parasitic. The stomachs of the first specimens found were full of fish flesh, as are those of most of the subsequent specimens. Evidence from the North Atlantic suggests that they feed on the flesh of halibut and other large fish, but probably only injured or moribund specimens. As *Simenchelys* only reaches a length of 28in (70cm) it is unlikely to be an active predator.

One further eel family (Aoteidae) may not exist at all. It was erected on the basis of one fish found inside the stomach of a snapper caught in Cook Strait (New Zealand) in 1926 and called *Aotea acus*. It was damaged and slightly digested, but could not be related to any previously described species. The corpse is elongate, scaleless, cylindrical, finless and has a wide mouth and a pointed snout. It is not known where the snapper had eaten it but it was presumed to be in deep water. No more have ever been found. *Aotea acus* has not been reexamined, but it may be the partially decomposed corpse of something else.

The remaining families in this order are all deep-sea eels and are modified for their environment in spectacular if different ways.

Members of the family of snipe eels are large-eyed, extremely elongated animals. The rear of the body is little more than a skin-covered continuation of the spine. Here the vertebrae are weak and poorly ossified, hence few complete specimens are known. One undamaged specimen, a lucky catch, has 670 vertebrae, the highest number known.

This family's common name alludes to its long and widely flaring jaws, fancifully seen as resembling the bill of the similarly named bird. It had been thought that there were two groups of snipe eels, those with extremely long divergent jaws and those with short divergent jaws. Recently enough specimens have been caught to show that mature males are short jawed and mature females and juveniles of both sexes are long jawed. Before maturity both the inside and outside of snipe eels' jaws are covered with small, backward-pointing teeth presenting a passable imitation of sandpaper. It seems likely that because adults have lost many teeth they eat little; possibly they die after they have reproduced.

Even when they have their granular teeth, how do snipe eels feed? The jaws can only close posteriorly. A few observations of living eels from deep-sea research submarine vessels have shown that they spend their time hanging vertically, mouth down, in the water, either still or with bodies gently undulating. A few specimens caught with food still in their stomachs revealed that the major food source is deep-sea shrimps. Characteristic of these are very long antennae and legs. It is suggested that snipe eels feed by entanglement, ie that once the

long antennae or legs of the crustacean become embrangled with the teeth inside or outside the jaws they are followed down to the body which is then consumed.

There are three recognized genera of snipe eels (*Avocettina*, *Nemichthys* and *Labichthys*). They are widely distributed in warmer parts of the oceans at depths down to 6,600ft (2,000m). The leptocephali are easily recognized by their thinness and the long caudal filament—a precursor of the adult's prolongation of the caudal region. They metamorphose when some 12in (30cm) long.

One of the most distinctive eels is the Curtailed snipe eel, probably a single-species family (Cyemidae). It looks somewhat like a dart with a long thin point divided into diverging dorsal and ventral parts. This eel occurs in all tropical and subtropical oceans at depths varying from 1,600 to 16,500ft (500–5,000m), but rarely as deep as the deepest figure. It is a laterally compressed, small fish, rarely exceeding 6in (15cm) long. It has a dark velvety skin and minute, but functional, eyes. Its biology is poorly known, though what is known of its breeding has some interesting aspects. Many eels breed in clearly circumscribed areas, where the physical conditions meet the stringent requirements of their physiology. By contrast in the Atlantic the Curtailed snipe eel spawns over large stretches of the warmer parts of the north Atlantic.

This eel's leptocephalus is quite different

▲ **Like an underwater snake.** There are about two hundred species of ophichthid or snake eels. They live in shallow, warm seas. Some have conspicuous colorings. Many burrow tail-first into the sea floor. This is *Myrichthys oculatus.*

◄ **Danger in the wings.** Moray eels are territorial and spend most of the day hidden in crevices with the head poking out to see what is happening. Normally if approached an eel retreats. If, however, the eel is provoked it may well bite. Some divers have been known to hand-feed morays for a while and then suddenly get bitten. An explanation for this is that the eel has mistaken the diver's hand for a favorite food item—the octopus. The Mediterranean moray can grow to over 6.5ft (2m) long and can inflict a nasty bite which, if by chance it severed an artery, could be fatal. Speared morays are very likely to attack because to a moray being speared counts as provocation. This is the Spotted moray (*Gymnothorax moringa*).

from that of others. Whereas the typical leptocephalus is a willow-leaf shape (save for minor variations), the leptocephalus of the Curtailed snipe eel can be nearly as deep as it is long. The little evidence available suggests that it spends at least two years in the larval phase.

On account of their mouths three families of deep-sea eels (Monognathidae, Saccopharyngidae and Eurypharyngidae) are sometimes grouped together under the name gulper eels. (Although three families are often recognized in the scientific literature there is growing evidence that fishes purportedly belonging to the Monognathidae may be young stages of fishes placed in the family Saccopharyngidae.) Monognathids are known from six species found in the Atlantic and Pacific oceans. Their scientific name, which means "one jawed," alludes to the fact that they lack upper jaw bones and have a conspicuous lower jaw which can be longer than the head. All known specimens are small. The largest known individual of

Monognathus jespersensi is only 4in (11cm) long but is only recently metamorphosed. Only one specimen, referred to *Monognathus isaacsi*, has developed any pigment. It seems likely that monognathids are juvenile saccopharyngids but adult saccopharyngids have many more vertebrae than the monognathids. However, the largest monognathids have the most vertebrae so perhaps vertebral formation continues as the fish grows. The conundrum will only be answered when either a sexually mature monognathid is discovered or when a clear monognathid–saccopharyngid transition series is built up.

Saccopharyngids are archetypal deep-sea fishes. They have huge mouths, elastic stomachs, toothed jaws and a luminous organ on the tail. An immediate enigma is that only four species are generally recognized whereas six species of monognathids are usually admitted. Therefore *if* monognathids are juvenile saccopharyngids then there are two more saccopharyngids awaiting discovery or

two monognathid species have been erroneously described.

Only one species from the western Atlantic has been seen alive (*Saccopharynx harrisoni*). This fortunate event happened because the fish, although trawled in 5,600ft (1,700m) of water, was not in the net but entangled by its teeth in the mouth of the trawl and so escaped being crushed by the weight of fish during the haul to the surface. Also, lacking a swim bladder, it escaped the fate of many deep-water

fishes—that of the considerable expansion of the gas in the swim bladder as the water pressure reduces towards the surface.

For deep-sea fishes saccopharyngids are large, growing to over 6.5ft (2m) long, but most of the body is tail. The huge mouth has necessitated some morphological changes. The gill arches are a long way behind the skull and dissociated into separate lateral halves. The opercular bones are not developed and the gill chambers are incompletely covered by skin. These modifications

▲ **The bright colors** and flaring, saucer-like nasal palps (the sensory appendages on the mouth) make the members of the genus *Rhinomuraena* popular with aquarists.

▶ **The remarkable jaws** of a deep sea snipe eel. They bear file-like teeth which entangle with the long legs and antennae of deep-sea crustaceans.

mean that its respiratory mechanism is unlike that of other fishes. Another peculiarity of these fishes, apart from the absence of a pelvic girdle, is that the lateral line organs, instead of lying in a sub-cutaneous canal, stand out from the body on separate papillae. It is surmised that this adaptation makes the fish more sensitive to vibrations in the water and enhances its chance of finding a suitable fish to cram into the distensible stomach. The escape of the prey, once in the mouth, is prevented by two rows of conical and curved teeth on the upper jaw and a single row of alternating large and small teeth on the lower jaw.

At the end of the long, tapering tail of all saccopharyngids there is a complex lumi-nous organ whose function is unknown. Indeed, the whole arrangement of the lumi-nous organs is odd. On the top of the head are two grooves that run backwards towards the tail. These contain a white, luminous tissue that glows with a pale light. The grooves separate to pass either side of the dorsal fin, each ray of which has two small, angled grooves containing a similar white tissue. The tail organ is confined to about the last 6in (15cm) of the body. Where the body is shallowest there is a single, pink, club-shaped tentacle on the ventral surface. Further back, where the body is more rounded, there are six dorsal and seven ventral scarlet projections (papil-lae) surmounting depigmented mounds. The main part of the organ lies behind these and is a transparent leaf-like structure with an ample supply of blood vessels. Its dorsal and ventral edges are prolonged and scarlet whereas the organ is pink because of the blood vessels. The main organ is split into two zones by a band of black pigment with red spots. Further finger-like papillae are even nearer the end of the body where the tail narrows and the black of the rest of the body is replaced by red and purple pigments. The small papillae produce a steady pink light. The leaf-like tail organ can produce flashes on top of a continuous reddish glow.

It is unlikely that the organ is a lure because the contortions required to place the organ where it will act as a lure, even for such a long, thin and presumably pre-hensile fish, would leave the body in a posi-tion where it would be unable to surge forwards to grasp the prey.

Equally bizarre is the last member of this group of deep-sea eels, the Gulper eel, the only member of its family. The mouth is big-ger than that of the saccopharyngids, and the jaws can be up to 25 percent of the body length. The jaws are joined by a black elastic membrane, the overall appearance of which prompted the trivial name *pelecanoides*, ie pelican-like. The eyes and brain are minute and confined to a very small area above the front of the mouth.

Almost nothing is known of its biology. The teeth are minute so it probably feeds on very small organisms. A small complex organ is present near the tail but it is not known if it is luminous. As in the saccopharyngids there is no swim bladder but there is an extensive liquid-filled lymphatic system which may aid buoyancy. The lateral line organs are external and show up as two or three papillae emerging from a small bump.

The larvae metamorphose at a small size, less than 1.5in (4cm), but even at this diminutive size have already developed the huge mouth. Interestingly the larvae live much nearer the surface of the sea (330–660ft, 100–200m) than the adults, which live at great depths.

The order of **notacanths** contains three families: Halosauridae, Notacanthidae and Lipogenyidae. All are scaled, deep-sea fishes rarely exceeding 6.5ft (2m) in length. They have a snout that extends in front of the mouth and which may be sharply pointed. The head is usually the deepest part of the body; the latter tapers away to a rat tail. In some species a minute caudal fin is present, in others the anal and caudal fins are confluent. The dorsal fin, if present, is short and placed well forward. The notacanths have a series of isolated spines on the back and in front of the anal fin.

The halosaurs live worldwide, mostly at depths down to 5,900ft (1,800m), but one species, *Aldrovandia rostrata*, was caught in 17,000ft (5,200m) of water in the North Atlantic. They feed on a wide range of invertebrates, mostly deep-dwelling forms which some notacanths are thought to dislodge from the sea bottom with their snouts. Other species include small squid in their diet and one species, *Halosauropsis macrochir* from the Atlantic, has a row of what are thought to be taste buds across the top of its head. They are mostly dark-hued fishes but *Halosaurus ovenii* is pinkish with silvery sheens. This species is also one of several in which the roof of the mouth has alternate light and dark stripes.

The notacanthids are stockier than the halosaurs and have a series of dorsal spines instead of a dorsal fin. They are distributed worldwide and feed on echinoderms, sponges and sea anemones from the sea floor.

The family Lipogenyidae contains only one species, *Lipogenys gilli* from the western North Atlantic. The main interest of this species is that it has a toothless mouth that functions like a vacuum cleaner and sucks up vast quantities of ooze. The amount of organic material in ooze is probably small but as this species has a long intestine, permitting maximum absorption of nutrients, it apparently survives on such an unpromising diet.

During a research voyage of 1928–30 the research vessel *Dana* caught, off South Africa, a leptocephalus larva 6ft (1.84m) long. Much speculation appeared in the popular and pseudoscientific press along the following lines: "if a 4in (10cm) conger eel leptocephalus produces an adult 6.5ft (2m) long, then this larva will produce an adult over 100ft (30m) long; hence it is a baby sea serpent and the sea serpent is an eel." Other giant leptocephali have been caught, and were named *Leptocephalus giganteus*. In the mid 1960s luck came to the aid of science. Another giant leptocephalus was caught but this time it was in mid metamorphosis and it could be established that the adult form was a notacanth. Reexamination of the other giant larvae showed they too could be referred to notacanths, thereby establishing the relationships of the notacanths with the eels and dispelling one set of rumors about sea serpents. Unlike other eels notacanths hardly grow after metamorphosis and the 100ft (30m) adult—the sea serpent—is merely a product of imaginative extrapolation.   KEB

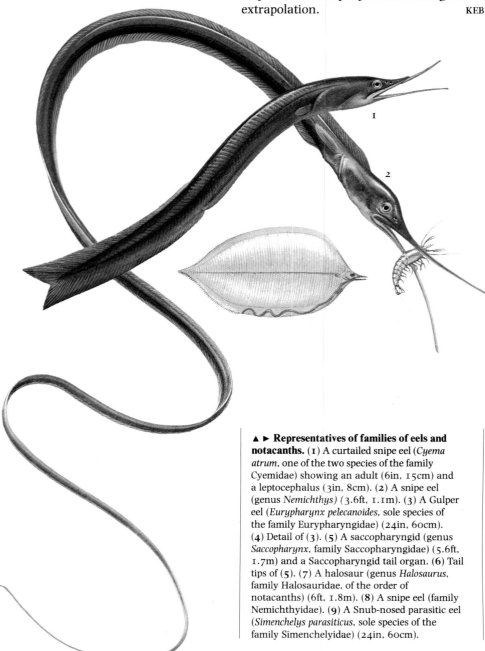

▲ ▶ **Representatives of families of eels and notacanths.** (1) A curtailed snipe eel (*Cyema atrum*, one of the two species of the family Cyemidae) showing an adult (6in, 15cm) and a leptocephalus (3in, 8cm). (2) A snipe eel (genus *Nemichthys*) (3.6ft, 1.1m). (3) A Gulper eel (*Eurypharynx pelecanoides*, sole species of the family Eurypharyngidae) (24in, 60cm). (4) Detail of (3). (5) A saccopharyngid (genus *Saccopharynx*, family Saccopharyngidae) (5.6ft, 1.7m) and a Saccopharyngid tail organ. (6) Tail tips of (5). (7) A halosaur (genus *Halosaurus*, family Halosauridae, of the order of notacanths) (6ft, 1.8m). (8) A snipe eel (family Nemichthyidae). (9) A Snub-nosed parasitic eel (*Simenchelys parasiticus*, sole species of the family Simenchelyidae) (24in, 60cm).

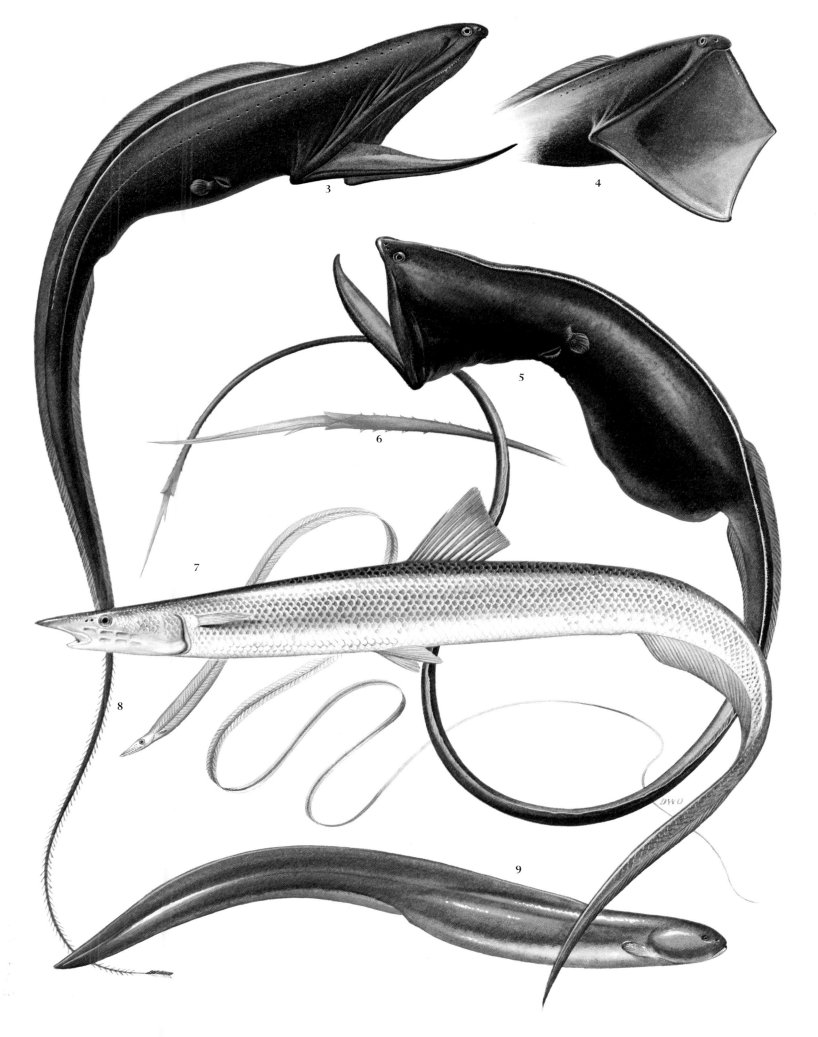

3

4

5

6

7

8

9

Fish Out of Water

How fishes are adapted for life on land

That humans are here reflects the fact that over 350 million years ago fish came out of water, adapted progressively to a terrestrial environment, evolved, and one of the results is us. Today various bony fishes leave the water for various lengths of time, although it is not suggested that the end point of their excursions will necessarily be as dramatic as that of their ancestors.

It must be pointed out that the ability of a fish to breathe air does not equate with its ability to leave water. The spectacular attributes of the lungfishes, among others, are dealt with elsewhere (see p134). Here we are concerned with fishes that actively travel out of water. Naturally there are degrees of extra-aquatic activity from small fishes that skitter along the water's surface momentarily to escape predation to the Pacific moray eel which may spend up to ten minutes out of water and others that spend far longer on land. What problems do they face?

Their problems are several. They include (*not* in order of severity): (1) respiration, (2) temperature control, (3) vision, (4) desiccation and (5) locomotion.

An initial problem facing fishes leaving water is that the surface area of the delicate gill filaments is reduced since they are no longer kept separate by the buoyancy of water. Drying out of the gills also occurs. Consequently other means of respiration have to be present and ways of protecting the gills. This usually involves the development of a sac into which the air is sucked, with a moist lining richly endowed with blood vessels (vascularized). As is always the case with fish, there are exceptions. The Chilean cling fish *Sicyaces sanguineus*, for example, which spends a substantial part of its life out of water, has a vascularized layer of skin in front of the sucker formed from its ventral fins. When it needs oxygen it raises the front of its body off the rocks and exposes this skin patch to the air. More "orthodox" are the anabantids (which include the Climbing perch) and the walking catfish (family Clariidae), which have pouches above the gill chamber, with linings expanded into convoluted shapes to increase the surface area. The Electric eel (*Electrophorus electricus*), which spends only a small part of its life out of water, can use its gills for aerial respiration, and the mud skippers (*Periophthalmus* species), which spend a lot of their life out of water, can use their skin.

Fishes on land have a problem in keeping cool. The difficulties are compounded because most "semiterrestrial" fish live in

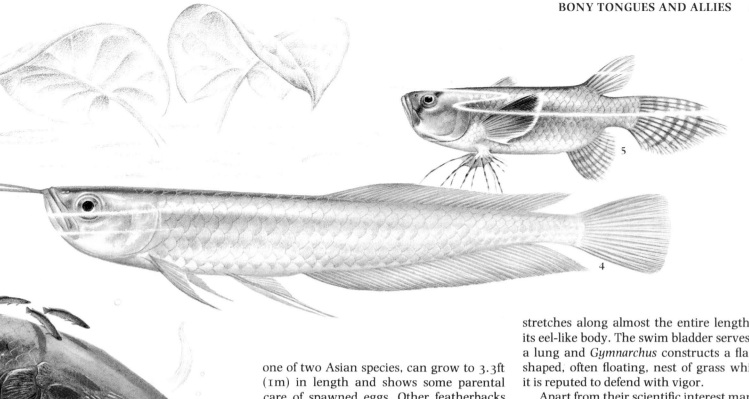

◀ ▲ **Representative species of bony tongues**
and allies. (**1**) *Petrocephalus catostoma*, a species
of elephant-snout (4in, 10cm). (**2**) An Elephant
mormyrid (*Campylomormyrus rhynchophorus*)
31in, 80cm). (**3**) An adult arapaima (*Arapaima
gigas*) (7.2ft, 2.2m) surrounded by juveniles.
(**4**) A juvenile bony tongue (genus
Osteoglossum) at the surface (4in, 10cm; adult
size 3.3ft, 1m). (**5**) A butterfly-fish (*Pantodon
buchholtzi*) (4in, 10cm).

one of two Asian species, can grow to 3.3ft
(1m) in length and shows some parental
care of spawned eggs. Other featherbacks
are smaller. Those of Africa, *Papyrocranus*
and *Xenomystus*, have accessory respiratory
structures above the gills and can inhabit
swampy pools. All of these fishes have large
mouths and predatory habits.

The **elephant-snouts** or mormyrids make
significant contributions to the fish stocks of
African lakes, rivers and floodpools. Most
are bottom dwellers feeding on worms,
insects and mollusks. Some are elephant-
snouted, but although there is a tendency
in others for a forward and downward prolongation of the snout region, within the
family head-shapes are highly variable.
Small to medium in size, all have small
mouths, eyes, gill-openings and scales. Dorsal and anal fins are set well back and the
deeply forked caudal fin has an exceptionally narrow peduncle. The muscles are
modified to form electric organs which produce a continuous field of weak discharges
at varying frequencies around the fish and
there are electro-reception centers in part of
the enlarged cerebellum of the brain (giving
mormyrids the largest brains to be found
among lower vertebrate animals). The
system as a whole acts as a sort of radar,
sensing distortions in the electrical field from
objects coming within it. This would seem
to be an ideal adaptation for nocturnal
activities, including social interactions, in
murky waters.

Much early research into electrogenic
activity was conducted on *Gymnarchus
niloticus*. Recently separated from the mormyrids by taxonomists, it is another large,
predaceous osteoglossomorph remarkable
for its shape. It lacks anal and caudal fins
and moves by undulating a dorsal fin which

stretches along almost the entire length of
its eel-like body. The swim bladder serves as
a lung and *Gymnarchus* constructs a flask-
shaped, often floating, nest of grass which
it is reputed to defend with vigor.

Apart from their scientific interest man is
involved with osteoglossomorphs at various
levels. There are capture fisheries for
Arapaima and *Osteoglossum* in South
America and for *Heterotis* and *Gymnarchus*
in the seasonal swamps and floodplains of
West Africa and the upper White Nile.
Larger mormyrids are more widely fished in
Africa, although they are not universally
acceptable as food. For example East African
women may forego them lest their children
are born with elephantine snouts. Bony
tongues, mooneyes and *Gymnarchus* are
rated as good sport fish by anglers and so
far as pond culture is concerned some progress has been made with representatives of
the group in each continent, namely the
arapaima, *Heterotis niloticus* and *Notopterus
chitala*. Good growth rates have been
achieved but in the case of *Heterotis* harvest-
ing may be thwarted by their superb ability
to leap an encircling seine net.

Pantodon, featherbacks and a number of
small mormyrids are particularly interesting for aquarists on account of their specialized features, but they are not
universally popular because breeding them
in captivity is either difficult or impossible.
Many public aquaria in the USA have
imported arapaima which at first caused
problems by attempting to swim through
the walls of tanks. In the Far East large specimens of *Scleropages* are also in captivity and
command astounding prices because of the
symbolism attached to them. In this connec-
tion it can be noted that *Gymnarchus* is an
important item in ceremonial feasts of the
Hausa people, and carved and painted mormyrids feature in the tombs of ancient
Egyptians.   RGB

PIKE, SALMON, ARGENTINES...

Order: Salmoniformes
Over three hundred species in 80 genera and
17 families.

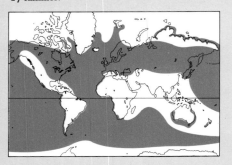

▶ **A small relative of the pike,** the European
mudminnow. Mudminnows feed on
invertebrates and small fish. Like the pikes they
have dorsal and anal fins set well back on the
body.

▼ **A lurking predator,** a Northern pike. This
species is widely distributed throughout the
cool, slow-flowing waters of the northern
hemisphere. Its staple prey is small fishes but
it also feasts on birds, frogs and other small
vertebrates. It is usually an inconspicuous
green but golden specimens are occasionally
found.

MEMBERS of the order of salmon, pike
and allies are of great interest to many
people. It contains prize angling fishes,
honored food fishes and fishes of great interest to biologists for their migratory habits.

The superorder Protacanthopterygii was
originally erected to contain primitive
teleostean fishes such as salmon, pike, lantern fishes, whale fishes and galaxiids.
Research in the last few years has shown
that these groups were "false friends,"
largely united on primitive characters
which do not indicate relationships. Consequently the superorder has been redefined
(though is probably still liable to change)
and is now limited to the old order Salmoniformes (see table).

The **pike, muskellunge and pickerels** are
famous game fishes, some of which grow to
a very large size and are known for their
ferocity once hooked. They are powerful and
aggressive predators, mostly on other fish,
and generally live solitary lives. They per-
form an important role in coarse-fish populations by controlling the numbers of
abundant, fast-breeding fish species of little
importance to anglers.

The distribution of pike is basically
circumpolar. Of the five species the Northern
pike is widespread in North America, Europe
and Asia, the others more local in range,
with one in Siberia and three in North
America. The biggest of them is the muskellunge or muskie which may reach more
than 66lb (30kg) and 5ft (1.5m) in length,
while the Northern pike may exceed 44lb
(20kg) and 3.3ft (1m). Legends of giant pike
abound (see p20).

The North American pickerels are
regarded by some experts as three species,
the Redfin pickerel, the Grass pickerel and
the Chain pickerel. Other authorities, however, regard the last two as subspecies of the
Redfin pickerel. All are small fishes, the Redfin and Grass pickerels rarely growing to
more than 1ft (30cm) long. The Chain pickerel is somewhat larger and in areas where
it cohabits with the others may hybridize
and produce fishes that are often claimed to
be Redfin or Chain pickerels of record size.
It is not always easy to distinguish the two
or three species, and even more difficult to
establish the true nature of the hybrids.

All pike species are similar in appearance,
being slender, elongate fish somewhat
laterally compressed with a long, flattened,
almost alligator-like snout. The mouth itself
is also long and has large pointed teeth.
Perhaps the most distinctive feature of pike
is the clustering of their dorsal and anal fins.
This concentration of finnage at the rear
enables them to accelerate rapidly and has
endowed them (and also other fish with
similar fin arrangements) with the name

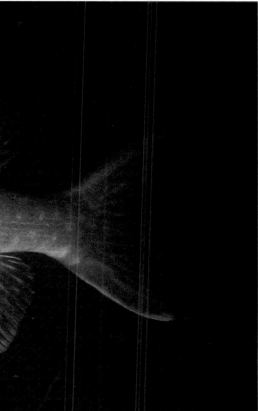

junct distribution is a relict one: fossils found in Europe and North America show that their former distribution was much like that of the extant pike. Today they occur in Europe, to the west of the Caspian Sea (European mudminnow); on the eastern side of North America (*Umbra pygmaea*, which has been introduced to Europe); in the Chelialis River, Washington, USA (*Novumbra hubbsi*); throughout the Great Lakes and Mississippi drainage (*Umbra limi*); and from Alaska and Eastern Siberia (the Alaskan black fish).

Mudminnows are small fishes, rarely exceeding 6in (15cm) in length. The caudal fin is rounded and the dorsal and anal fins are set far back, as in the pike. Their coloring is cryptic—mottled dark brown or olivaceous. All are carnivorous and feed on small invertebrates and larval fishes which they seize by making rapid lunges. They are sluggish, retiring fishes, hiding away among weeds waiting for the prey to come within striking distance.

Mudminnows are capable of living in high densities in poorly oxygenated swampy areas as they can utilize atmospheric oxygen. They are tolerant of drought, which they escape by burrowing into soft mud and ooze, and also tolerate cold, especially the Alaskan black fish, much as one might expect from where it lives. In many books there are accounts of the Alaskan black fish being able to withstand freezing. This frequently repeated untruth seems to stem from a book written by L.M. Turner in 1886. In *Contributions to the natural history of Alaska* . . . he wrote: "The vitality of this fish is astonishing. They will remain in . . . grass buckets for weeks, and when brought in the house and thawed out they will be as lively as ever. The pieces which are thrown to the ravenous dogs are eagerly swallowed; the animal heat of the dog's stomach thaws the fish out, whereupon its movements cause the dog to vomit it up alive. This I have *seen* . . ." Sadly for sensation, properly controlled experiments have shown that although the Alaskan black fish is capable of living at very low temperatures, it cannot survive freezing or being ice-bound.

The **galaxiids** (they have no common name) are distinctive small fishes found in all the major southern land masses (Australia, New Zealand, South America and South Africa) and also on some of the more remote southern islands like New Caledonia, Auckland and Campbell and the Falklands. The first galaxiid was collected by naturalists with Captain Cook in New Zealand during 1777. The name *Galaxias* was given to the

"lurking predators." They skulk among vegetation around the margins of lakes and streams and surge out to catch passing prey.

Pike are mainly freshwater fish, but a few venture into mildly saline waters in Canadian lakes and the Baltic. Spawning takes place among vegetation in still or gently flowing marginal shallows. The female pairs with a male and the two spend several hours together releasing and fertilizing small batches of quite large eggs (about 1in, 2.5–3cm long). A large female may lay several hundred thousand eggs. From the time they hatch pike are predators, initially eating insects and small crustaceans but very soon becoming fish-eaters like the adults. Large pike may also occasionally take small mammals and birds.

Pike are prized by anglers, especially in Europe. In North America, where salmon species are more diverse, abundant and freely available the popularity of pike is not as great though many fishermen have the aspiration of catching a large muskellunge.

The **mudminnows** are closely related to pike. They were formerly included in the families Daliidae and Novumbridae, but are now united in one family. Their present dis-

fish, because it was dark, black-olive and covered with a profusion of small gold spots resembling a galaxy of stars. Galaxiids are fish of distinctive appearance. Scaleless, they have smooth leathery skins. Unlike some northern relatives they have no adipose fin but have the single dorsal fin well back towards the tail, over the anal fin. Most are small, 4–10in (10–25cm) in length, but one reaches 23in (58cm), while there are several tiny species, 1–2in (3–5cm) long. Most species are tubular, cigar-shaped fish with blunt heads, thick fleshy fins and a truncated tail. A few are stocky, thick-bodied fish and most of these are secretive fish that skulk among boulders, logs or debris in streams or lakes. Many are solitary but a few are shoaling fish. All but about six species are freshwater fish and a few are marine migratory fish in which the larval and juvenile phases are spent at sea.

Migratory species spawn mostly in fresh water, rarely in estuaries. When their eggs hatch tiny larvae, about 0.4in (1cm) long, are swept to sea. Their ability to cope with a sudden transition from fresh to sea water shows remarkable flexibility. They spend 5–6 months at sea before migrating back into fresh waters during spring, as elongate transparent juveniles. It will be months before these fish reach maturity, at about a year in some species, two to three years in others.

What is known about the spawning of these fish is equally remarkable. One species, Galaxias maculatus, is known to spawn in synchrony with the lunar or tidal cycle, spawning over vegetated estuary margins during high spring tides. When these high tides retreat the eggs are stranded in the vegetation and protected from dehydration only by humid air. Development takes place out of water, the eggs not being reimmersed until the next set of spring tides two weeks later. Then the eggs hatch, releasing the larvae which are swept quickly out to sea. Another species, which lives in small heavily forested streams, spawns during floods. This fish, Galaxias fasciatus, deposits its eggs in leaf litter along stream margins. When the floods dissipate the eggs are left stranded among rotting leaves, where they develop. Hatching cannot occur until there is a further flood and then the larvae are swept downstream and out to sea.

It is clear that both these modes of spawning involve substantial risks. The breeding habits described above are exceptional. As far as is known most galaxiid species lay their eggs in clusters between rocks and boulders. A few very small species pair up for spawning and lay their eggs on the leaves of aquatic plants.

Although the southern lands in which these fish occur tend to have moist climates, some species have become adapted to surviving droughts and therefore aestivate. Some live in pools that lie on the floor of wet podocarp forests in water usually only a few centimeters deep which covers leaf litter shed from the towering forests above. In the late summer and fall these pools frequently dry up and the fish disappear into natural hollows around the buttresses of trees. They survive for several weeks in these damp pockets until rainfall restores water to the forest floor. The fish wait for the return of water before spawning. As the pools are increasingly replenished larvae are enabled to disperse around the forest floor and invade available habitats.

Historically the very broad distribution of the galaxiid fishes has attracted intense interest. Long ago zoologists asked how a group of freshwater fish could be so widely distributed around southern lands. Not only is the family widely dispersed but one species, Galaxias maculatus, is found in Australia, Tasmania, Lord Howe Island, New Zealand, Chatham Islands, Chile, Argentina and the Falkland Islands. With such a broad range this fish is one of the naturally most widely distributed freshwater fish known. Noting the remarkable range of this species, zoologists of the late 19th century suggested that there must have been former land connections between the areas where the fish are present. Some thought that Antarctica might have been involved.

In recent years it has been suggested that the distribution of galaxiid fishes results from their former presence on the southern continent Gondwanaland. This huge land mass was breaking apart some 70 million years ago. If galaxiid fishes were then present their distribution could date back to these ancient times, but this view is debatable. An alternative interpretation is that they dispersed through the sea to attain their present distribution. The latter viewpoint becomes more acceptable when it is remembered that some species spend up to six months at sea. It is probably no coincidence that the widely distributed species are also the sea-going ones.

That such small fish should have attained importance for commercial fisheries may seem remarkable. However, when European settlers arrived in New Zealand in the mid 19th century they found that vast populations of the sea-living juveniles of several Galaxias species migrated into rivers during

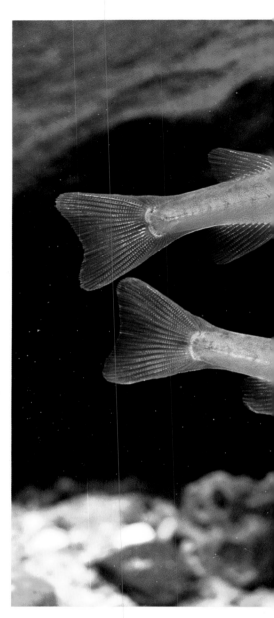

▲ **Scattered across the southern hemisphere** are the galaxiids, about 40 species of mostly freshwater fishes. They are the southern relatives of the salmons and trouts. Their enigmatic distribution has caused much speculation. One school favors the theory that they dispersed along ocean currents. Another argues that they developed from fishes that were separated when the great southern continent Gondwanaland broke up some 70 million years ago. This is one of the 20 Australian species, the Flathead galaxias (Galaxias rostratus).

▶ **The markings on some galaxiids,** like the Golden galaxias (Galaxias auratus) shown here, resemble the specklings on the northern trouts. This species is restricted to Lakes Crescent and Sorell and associated streams in Tasmania.

spring. The Maoris of New Zealand exploited huge quantities of them and not surprisingly the Europeans followed their example, calling the tiny fish whitebait on account of their similarity to fish they knew at home in England. Quantities caught today do not compare with those of the early years, but a good fishery persists in some rivers. Colossal numbers of fish are caught (each weighing only about 0.02oz—there are about 800 fishes to a pound). The catches of individual fishermen vary from just a few to many pounds, exceptional catches reaching several hundred pounds in a day. Not only are these a delicious gourmet seafood, but they may sell for up to 25 Australian dollars a pound in the shops.

The family of **salmon, trout, charrs and their relatives** contains some of the most prestigious and influential fishes of the northern hemisphere. Included here are the Atlantic and Pacific salmon, trout, charrs, grayling and whitefish.

Of this august company the Atlantic salmon is the best known. Many people pay high prices for its flesh and even higher prices for the pleasure of trying to catch it by inefficient means. It is caught more efficiently by commercial fishermen (ensuing problems are discussed on pp18–19). Although salmon is now a luxury item, in the 19th century apprentices in London protested about being fed salmon six days a week.

To emphasize the significance of the only salmon species native to the Atlantic, just think of the different names applied to each stage of its life history. On hatching they are called fry and alevins. Later, when they are a few inches long and have developed

dark blotches on the body, they are parr (the blotches are parr marks). When they make for the sea the marks become covered by a silvery pigment and they are called smolt. When the adult male returns early from the sea it is a grilse. The adults, spent after spawning, and drifting back to sea, are called kelt.

After adult salmon have spawned in their home streams (see box) the eggs remain in the gravel, for much of the winter in the case of the early run salmon. Hatching time can be calculated on the 440 day-degree principle, ie when the average water temperature in degrees Celsius multiplied by the number of days since spawning equals 440, the eggs hatch. This is usually in April–May in northern Europe.

The young are about 0.8in (2cm) long on hatching and for the first six weeks or so live in the gravel, feeding on their yolk sacs. With the exhaustion of the yolk supply they emerge from the gravel and start feeding on insect larvae and other invertebrates. As they grow they develop into parr and their markings give them camouflage for hunting actively. The length of time spent in fresh water varies from five years in the north of the range to one year in the south.

Not all members of the year class migrate to the sea. A few males stay in fresh water and become precociously mature. These have been seen shedding sperm in the company of mating adults and it is argued that the precocious males act as a security in case no males return from the sea. The migrating young spend some time in estuaries, acclimatizing themselves for coping with salt water. In the sea they grow rapidly and can reach 30lb (14kg) in 3 years. They feed on fish and spend up to four years in the sea building up strength for the rigors of the spawning migration. When returning to the natal stream for spawning they can travel 70 miles (115km) a day.

There are a few populations of land-locked salmon in lakes in the far north of America and Europe. They never grow as large as the others but still run up streams to spawn. It is thought that their access to the sea was stopped after the last ice age.

There are probably seven species of the Pacific salmon, whose generic name (*Oncorhynchus*) means hooked snout. Their life history is very similar to that of the Atlantic salmon. Two species have land-locked forms, first the Sockeye salmon, which is found from southern Oregon to Japan, and the somewhat doubtful species *Oncorhynchus rhodiurus* from Lake Biwa in Japan.

▲ **Driven by an irresistible compulsion,** adult salmon returning to the spawning ground can make prodigious leaps to overcome obstacles.

◄ **At the spawning ground** TOP the female salmon (here a Sockeye salmon) scrapes out a nest in the gravel of the river bed.

◄ **The large yolky eggs** CENTER are normally hidden in the gravel to hide them from predators.

◄ **Newly hatched salmon young** BELOW LEFT are called alevins or fry.

▼ **Young salmon** feed on their yolk sac at first. When this is almost exhausted, as shown here, they start to feed on small invertebrates.

▷ **A silvery school** OVERLEAF of Atlantic salmon. It was once one of the most widespread species in river systems draining into the Atlantic, until the rise of pollution, poaching and gross overfishing.

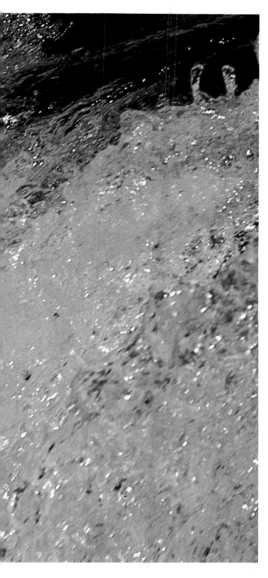

In the Atlantic Ocean the Atlantic salmon grows to about 70lb (32kg) in weight. The Chinook salmon has been recorded at 126lb (57kg). The Humpback or Pink salmon rarely grows to more than 20lb (9kg) but only takes two years to mature.

A Eurasian genus is *Hucho*. It includes the huchen, a slender species from the Danube; others occur in Central Asia. Attempts were made to translocate the huchen to the Thames in the 19th century. Despite rumors of it surviving into the early 20th century there is no reliable evidence that the introduction succeeded. The introduction of the Pink salmon into the northwest Atlantic, however, was an accident and the range of this Pacific species is continually expanding.

The charrs come from the cold deep lakes and rivers of Europe and North America. Only in the very north of the Atlantic are they migratory. The sole European species, *Salvelinus alpinus*, is very variable. Until relatively recently a different species was named from almost each lake. In the breeding season the males sport a spectacular deep red on the breast. If anything their flesh exceeds that of the salmon in quality and those lucky enough to have the chance to sample it should have charr steaks, lightly boiled with bay leaves, cold on toast.

Despite its common name of Brook trout, this eastern American species is a charr. In its native haunts the migratory form can grow to nearly 3ft (90cm) long but the European introductions rarely reach half that length. In Europe, the Brook trout hybridizes with both the native Brown trout and the introduced Rainbow trout. The offspring of both mismatches are a striped fish called the tiger or zebra trout. They are sterile.

The European brown trout has caused much confusion in the past among anglers and fishmongers. It is a very variable species, both in form and behavior, so consequently has been given many common names: eg trout, River trout, Lake trout, Salmon trout and Sea trout. Brown trout that live in lakes may become very large and cannibalistic—these are Lake trout. Brown trout that migrate to the sea to feed become very silvery and are called Sea trout or Salmon trout (*not* a hybrid between a salmon and a Brown trout). As a result of the richer feeding possibilities in the sea, the migratory Brown trout reach nearly twice the size of their nonmigratory brothers. What is not understood is why, when some populations of Brown trout could migrate to sea, they do not.

A similar situation occurs on the western coast of North America with the Rainbow trout. This commonly introduced denizen

Return to Base

The life history of the Atlantic salmon exemplifies that of the other anadromous species (ie those that migrate from the sea to fresh water to spawn). Larger salmon run up rivers in winter, smaller ones in summer, overcoming most obstacles to return to the stream in which they were hatched (this may be a journey of thousands of miles for the Pacific salmons). The key to this remarkable ability is memory and a sense of smell. It has been demonstrated that the adults remember the smell of their birth stream (a combination of chemicals in the water contributed by the rocks, soils, vegetation etc) and can find it again. Naturally, occasional errors are made, or the return route is blocked as a result of dam construction or drought, which enables the species to extend its range.

The males usually arrive back first, but the females normally select the spawning site, where they are aggressively courted by the males. During maturation the colors of the males are enhanced and the lower jaw bends upwards to form a hook called the kype. The spawning site (called a redd) is excavated in gravel by the vigorous movements of the female's tail until it is up to 10ft (3m) long and 12in (30cm) deep. The pair lie alongside each other for spawning and accompany the act

with much trembling and jaw opening. Each act of spawning continues for about five minutes and the whole process may continue for a fortnight. In between, the adults rest in deep holes in the river bed. After each spawning session the redd is filled in and another excavated.

When all the eggs are shed the adults drift slowly back to sea, exhausted and prone to many infections. One of the mysteries of Atlantic salmon migrating upstream to spawn

is that they do not feed in fresh water (hence the understandable exhaustion and loss of up to 40 percent of body weight), yet they are caught on anglers' spoons and spinners. Why they are tempted to ingest these flashing objects is unknown. Very few males survive spawning, but those that do will recover rapidly in the rich feeding grounds in the sea. Only a tiny number of females have survived four spawnings. KEB

of fish farms in Europe has an extensive natural range from southern California to Alaska. In the northern part of its range it is migratory, and much larger and more intensively colored than in the south. The Canadians call it the Steelhead trout (migratory form) whereas the nonmigratory is the Rainbow. Some years ago a water authority in the United Kingdom bought from North America a large number of Rainbow trout to enhance the trout fishing in their waters. Unfortunately they were provided with the migratory form, and very little of their investment ever returned.

Because of their sporting and palatable qualities salmon and trout have been introduced into many countries. The Brown trout is now found in the North American west, doubtless in exchange for the Rainbow trout, and in almost all southern hemisphere countries, even in some tropical ones where there are cool streams at high altitudes in which they can thrive.

If the naming of trout species formerly caused chaos it is nothing compared with the current chaos concerning the whitefish. These are relatively plain, silvery salmonoids, the great majority of which live in cold deep lakes of Asia and northern America. (A few species are also found in Europe.) There are probably three genera. Many species are highly variable. For example populations in European lakes have been grouped into any number from three to eight species. They are of economic importance, especially in North America where they are smoked. A few species are migratory, but most are landlocked as a result of hydrological changes and changes in sea level since the last ice age.

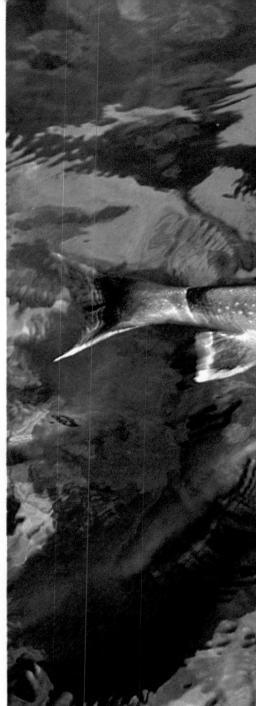

▲ **The huchen** LEFT is a species of salmon from the River Danube and its tributaries. Attempts to introduce it to other rivers have been unsuccessful. It eats aquatic vertebrates and invertebrates but will also feed sporadically on other food, eg small mammals.

▲ **The charrs** ABOVE live in cold northern waters. In the breeding season the underside turns a bright red. This is the European charr (*Salvelinus alpinus*).

◄ **The Rainbow trout** derives its common name from the stripe on its flanks. Native to North America it has now been introduced to many parts of the world, often to the detriment of the local fauna.

► **The Brook trout,** a native of North America now introduced to Europe, is despite its common name a charr.

The graylings derive their generic name (*Thymallus*) from the thyme-like smell of their flesh. They are fishes of cool, swift-flowing rivers. Occasionally they enter brackish water. *Thymallus thymallus* is widespread in Europe and Asia. The slightly more colorful *Thymallus arcticus* occurs in northern America. In northern Asia some dubious species have been described.

To complete this important family two more poorly known species of uncertain affinities must be mentioned. In the lakes of the Ohrid region on the borders of Albania, Yugoslavia and Greece live salmonoids placed in the genus *Salmothymus*. They may be southern landlocked salmons. The genus *Brachymystax* comes from rivers of Mongolia, China and Korea. No satisfactory conclusions have been reached on its relationships—very few specimens have ever been available for study.

The family of scaled, cylindrical, southern hemisphere salmonoids are commonly known as **southern graylings**. Only two species are included in this family: *Prototroctes oxyrhynchus* from New Zealand and *P. maraena* from southeastern Australia and Tasmania. The New Zealand species was first described and named in 1870 when it was abundant. The last known specimens were caught by accident in a Maori fish trap in 1923. It is presumed to be extinct.

The Australian species appears to be following the same path; it is now described as severely endangered. Why these two remarkable fish species should have suffered so is unknown. In New Zealand they disappeared from regions completely untouched by human development, as well as from those areas where the cause was evident. When Europeans first settled in New Zealand in the 1860s *Prototroctes* was abundant and regarded as a good source of food, but by the late 1870s there was already concern about the decline of this widespread fish. In 1900 they were described as "thinned out." Twenty-three years later the last known specimens were caught. Once they existed in their millions; today there are less than 40 bodies preserved in the great national museums of the world—and a stuffed specimen in the Rotoiti Lodge of the New Zealand Deer Stalkers' Association, Nelson.

There are only a few records describing the New Zealand *Prototroctes* alive. Like its Australian congener it had only one ovary or testis. The early reports of its body color are inconsistent. One suggests that it was slaty on the back, merging to silvery on the sides and belly with patches of azure. The

fins were orange, slaty dark at the tips and the cheeks had a golden tinge. It seemed to have migrated regularly from the sea to fresh water where it spawned.

Aplochiton zebra is a fairly widespread fish, occurring in rivers of Patagonia and the Falkland Islands where it is called trout. Unlike the inconspicuously colored *Prototroctes*, *Aplochiton* has dark vertical stripes over the back and sides of its scaleless body. Its persistence in the Falkland Islands has been placed in jeopardy by the introduction of the Brown trout from Europe—a sad fate for a species first collected by Charles Darwin when he visited the Falklands. Very little is known of the biology of this fish.

The **osmerids** or smelts may well have acquired their alternative common name from the fact that a fresh *Osmerus eperlanus*, the northern European species, has a strong smell (like that of a cucumber). Even if apocryphal, it is a pleasing idea. Mostly small, silvery fish, smelts live in coastal and brackish cool waters in the northern hemisphere. Numerous, probably landlocked populations are known. They are carnivores, feeding on small invertebrates seized with their sharp conical teeth.

Their importance to subsistence fisheries in the far north is significant. They can be numerous and have a high fat content. When not eaten by the original inhabitants of the British Columbian coast, they were dried, and because of their fat content could be set alight and used as a natural candle. Hence *Thaleichthys pacificus* now has the common name of Candle fish.

The **ayu** is the only species in its family. This very peculiar salmonoid lives in Japan and adjacent parts of Asia, where it is of great economic importance. Its body is olive brown with a pale yellow blotch on the side. The dorsal fin is expanded and, like the other fins, has a reddish tint. When these colors, especially the reds, are enhanced in the breeding season, the Japanese name for the fish changes from *ayu* to *sabi*, which means rusty. Instead of the male developing an extended snout (kype) as many salmonoid males do, both sexes become covered in warty "nuptial tubercules" (warty growths) at the onset of breeding. The upper jaw of the male shortens and the female's anal fin expands. These changes start during the summer and the fish breed in the fall.

The fish mature in the upper reaches of rivers and, unlike most other salmonoids, move downstream towards the sea to breed. Little is known about their breeding behavior. Some 20,000 adhesive eggs are produced which hatch in about three weeks,

A Pike in the Southern Hemisphere?

If the galaxiids are the salmonoids of the southern hemisphere, and salmonoids are related to pike, is there a southern hemisphere pike? The answer is probably yes.

Described as recently as 1961, it is a small fish found in numerous localities in southern Australia and called *Lepidogalaxias salamandroides*. It was originally thought to be a galaxiid, but unlike galaxiids it has scales, dorsal and anal fins set much further forward and the anal fin of the mature male is highly modified with gnarled and hooked rays and peculiar dermal flaps.

This tiny fish, about 1.5in (4cm) long, has recently been much studied and the general, but not universal, conclusion is that it is more closely related to the northern hemisphere pikes than to the southern hemisphere galaxiids.

Little is known of its biology. It is apparently capable of surviving drought by burrowing in mud or under damp leaves. Its distribution appears to be confined to small pools and ditches mostly in the sand-plain area between the Scott River and Lake Powell. It is usually found in acid water (with a pH up to 4.5).   KEB

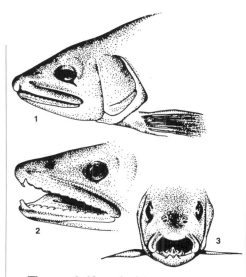

▲ **The remarkable teeth of the ayu.**
(1) Juxtaposing comb teeth on the outside of the jaw. (2) The fleshy snout with the few canine teeth behind it. (3) The canine teeth and the elaborate skin folds inside the mouth. The ayu's actual method of feeding is only known from supposition.

▼ **Named for its smell.** The scientific name of the European grayling (*Thymallus thymallus*) alludes to the thyme-like smell of its flesh, which is delicious though it soon deteriorates after the fish's death. For this reason graylings have virtually no commercial importance.

depending on temperature. The larvae stay in the river until they are about 1in (2.5cm) long when they move into the sea.

This seaward migration of the larvae is part of an interesting survival strategy. If the young stayed in the river, having spawned in the fall, they would have to endure the cold and compete with larger young of the species that spawned in spring (when most fishes spawn). However, during winter the temperature of the sea is more stable than that of the river and at sea food is more abundant. On the other hand, the young ayu have to have developed a physiological (osmotic) mechanism to enable their small bodies to cope with the shock of transferring from fresh to salt water. They must be able to cope with the transfer but it is not known how. During winter they feed on zooplankton and small crustaceans and, by spring, when they reenter fresh water, they have grown to about 3in (8cm) long. They they migrate upstream in huge shoals, when thousands are caught and taken to capture ponds to facilitate a rapid growth rate and to provide an easily accessible source of food. The fish that escape continue up to the fast-flowing upper reaches, where each fish establishes a territory for itself among rocks and stones. Here they feed on diatoms and algae until summer or fall when they move downstream to spawn. The ayu is an annual fish as almost all adults die after spawning. The few adults that survive spawning (a very small percentage) spend the winter at sea and repeat the cycle.

Concomitant with the change of diet from young to adult and the move from salt to fresh water, the teeth change drastically. While the ayu is at sea its diet is typically salmonoid: using its conical teeth it catches small crustaceans and other invertebrates. Adults, by contrast, feed on algae and have a whole series of groups of teeth forming comb-like structures. Even more unusual is the fact that the teeth lie outside the mouth.

The comb-teeth develop under the skin of the jaw and erupt, shedding the conical teeth, when the fish enter fresh water. Each comb-tooth consists of 20–30 individual teeth, each one shaped like a crescent on a stick: narrow in the plane of the fish but very broad transversely. The gutter of the crescent faces inwards and, because of the different lengths of the arms of the crescent on each tooth, forms a sinuous gutter across the width of the comb-teeth. The combs of the upper and lower jaws juxtapose outside the mouth when it is closed. At the front of each lower jaw is a bony, pointed process that fits into a corresponding recess in the

upper jaw. On the mid-line of the floor of the mouth is a flange of tissue, which is low at the front but higher at the back where it branches into two. Each branch bends back on itself to run forwards, parallel to the sides of the jaw and decreasing in height towards the front. Muscles link this device with a median bone in the branchial series.

It is known that adult ayus eat algae, but how? "Grazing marks" have been seen on stones covered by algae in an ayu's territory. It is usually stated that they are formed by the comb-like teeth, but as these teeth are outside the jaw, any algae so scraped off would be washed away and not eaten. Even to make the grazing marks would necessitate the fish lying on its side, a maneuver that it is most unlikely to make in a swift current.

It is suggested here that the ayu is a filter-feeder in a manner analogous to that of the baleen whales. The ayu's snout is fleshy and slightly overhangs the front of the upper jaw. Behind the snout, at the front of the upper jaw, is a row of about eight small conical teeth. Hanging down from the palate is a complex series of curtain-like structures which have a relationship to the various flanges on the floor of the mouth. It is possible that if the ayu were to face into the current and scrape the algae off the rocks with the conical teeth, the algae so scraped would wash into the mouth. This would at least offer a reasonable explanation for the grazing marks and, with its large mouth and wide gape, the ayu is theoretically capable of performing this maneuver. With enough algae inside, the mouth could be tightly closed. (Certainly with the peg and socket fitments at the front and the clean, straight toothless abutting parts of the upper and lower jaws the mouth is designed to close firmly.) When sealed, if the muscles mentioned above were contracted, the floor of the mouth would be brought up to the palate, thus squeezing out the water. The algal particles would be trapped on the hanging fringes and could be swallowed. How they are swallowed is unknown. If the comb-teeth are a part of the filtration system they can only act as a long-stop, but if so, how the entrapped particles are removed is a mystery.

The shape of the teeth suggests that they ought to have some filtering function, but if it turns out that they do not, then we have to find another explanation for the presence of these peculiar yet highly evolved structures. Indeed, much work remains to be done on this enigmatic, yet commercially important, species.

THE 17 FAMILIES OF PIKE, SALMON, ARGENTINES AND ALLIES

Superfamily: ESOCOIDEA

Pike, muskellunge, pickerels and their relatives

Family: Esocidae
Five species of the genus *Esox*.
Distribution: fresh waters of Northern Hemisphere mostly N of 40 degrees N, but largely absent from USA W of Mississippi basin.
Size: maximum length 5ft (1.5m), maximum weight 66lb (30kg).
Species: **Chain pickerel** (*Esox niger*), **Grass pickerel** (*E. vermiculatus*), **muskellunge** or **muskie** (*E. masquinongy*), **Northern pike** (*E. lucius*), **Redfin pickerel** (*E. americanus*).

Mudminnows
Family: Umbridae
Five species in 3 genera.
Distribution: N America, E Europe, USSR W of Caspian Sea and E Siberia.
Size: maximum length 6in (15cm).
Species include: **Alaskan black fish** (*Dallia pectoralis*), **European mudminnow** (*Umbra kraemeri*).

Superfamily: LEPIDOGALAXOIDEA

Family: Lepidogalaxiidae
Lepidogalaxias salamandroides.
Distribution: S Australia, in sand plain area between R Scott and Lake Powell.
Size: length 1.5in (4cm).

Superfamily: SALMONOIDEA

Galaxiids
Family: Galaxiidae
About forty species in 6 genera.
Distribution: S America, S Africa, Australia, New Zealand, southern islands, eg New Caledonia, Falkland Islands.
Size: length 1–22in (3–57cm).

Salmon, trout, charrs and their relatives

Family: Salmonidae
About seventy species in 10 genera.
Distribution: northern temperate and subarctic fresh waters.
Size: maximum length 5ft (1.5m).
Species and genera include: **Atlantic salmon** (*Salmo salar*), **Brook trout** (*Salvelinus fontinalis*), **Brown trout** (*Salmo trutta*), **charrs** (genus *Salvelinus*), **Chinook salmon** (*Oncorhynchus tshawytscha*), **graylings** (genus *Thymallus*), **Humpback** or **Pink salmon** (*Oncorhynchus gorbuscha*), **Pacific salmon** (genus *Oncorhynchus*), **Rainbow trout** (*Salmo gairdneri*), **Sockeye salmon** (*Oncorhynchus nerka*),

whitefish (genera *Coregonus, Prospium, Stenodus*).

Southern graylings*

Family: Prototroctidae
Two species of the genus *Prototroctes*.
Distribution: SE Australia, Tasmania, New Zealand.
Size: maximum adult length 14in (35cm).

Family: Aplochitonidae*
Probably four species in 2 genera.
Distribution: Patagonia, Falkland Islands.
Size: length 12in (30cm).

Superfamily: OSMEROIDEA

Smelts or osmerids

Family: Osmeridae
Ten or eleven species in probably 6 genera.
Distribution: Northern Hemisphere in Atlantic and Pacific oceans in coastal and brackish waters.
Size: maximum adult length 16in (40cm) but most are less than half this size.
Species include: **Candle fish** (*Thaleichthys pacificus*).

Ayu

Family: Plecoglossidae
Plecoglossus altivelis.
Distribution: Japan and adjacent parts of Asia in marine and fresh waters.
Size: about 12in (30cm).

Southern smelts

Family: Retropinnidae
Four species in 2 genera.
Distribution: southern Australia, Tasmania, New Zealand in fresh, coastal and marine waters.
Size: maximum adult length 6in (15cm).

Noodle fishes or ice fishes

Family: Salangidae
About fourteen species in 6 genera.
Distribution: SE Asia and offshore areas in estuary and marine waters.
Size: 7in (18cm).

Family: Sundasalangidae
Two species of the genus *Sundasalanx*.
Distribution: southern Thailand and Borneo in fresh water.
Size: probably less than 1in (2.5cm).

Superfamily: ARGENTINOIDEA

Argentines or herring smelts

Family: Argentinidae
Twenty species in 2 or 3 genera.
Distribution: Atlantic, Indian and Pacific oceans.
Size: maximum length about 24in (60cm).

Family: Bathylagidae
Probably thirty-five species in 3 genera.
Distribution: Atlantic and Pacific oceans in deep water.
Size: 10in (25cm).

Superfamily: ALEPOCEPHALOIDEA

Slickheads

Family: Alepocephalidae
At least sixty species in about 22 genera.
Distribution: all oceans.
Size: maximum adult length 30in (76cm) but many are smaller.

Family: Bathyprionidae
Bathyprion danae.
Distribution: N and SE Atlantic Ocean, S Indian Ocean.
Size: 18in (45cm).

Family: Searsiidae
About thirty species in about 12 genera.
Distribution: all oceans.
Size: maximum length probably 15in (38cm).

*Some authors place these families within the southern smelts (Retropinnidae).

► **Top sport** ABOVE, a giant Pacific salmon caught by a North American fisherman.

► **An uncertain future** BELOW faces the Australian species of southern grayling. During the last 40 years its numbers have fallen dramatically. Now it is severely endangered. Its New Zealand relative has not been seen for well over 50 years and is deemed extinct.

The **southern smelts** are slender, small-mouthed fishes from southeastern Australia, Tasmania and New Zealand. Some populations are migratory, others landlocked. Because they are very variable in form their taxonomy is far from clear. There may be three Australian species, or just one, which may or may not be the same species as *Retropinna retropinna* of New Zealand.

Noodle fishes are very small, slender transparent fishes from the western Pacific. Although marine they move into estuaries to spawn. Their head is tiny and pointed and the deepest part of the body is just in front of the dorsal fin. The only coloration on the 4in (10cm) long *Salangichthys microdon* is two rows of small black spots on the belly. Although small, they are sometimes so abundant that they can easily be caught for food. To the Japanese they are a delicacy called *shirauwo*.

The shape and transparency of the adult is very similar to that of the larvae of other, larger salmonoids. If it were not for the fact that sexually mature examples are known, they would have been thought to be larvae. It is not unknown in lower vertebrates for a species to evolve by a process called neoteny or paedomorphosis in which the body development is curtailed whilst sexual development is not. Both this family and the following one are neotenic. The best known example of neoteny occurs in the axolotl, which is the sexually mature, reproducing, former larva of a salamander. With time the ability to "grow up" is lost and a new species formed.

The two very small freshwater species that form the family Sundasalangidae, from Thailand and Borneo, were described as recently as 1981. The body is scaleless and transparent. Although they have the posteriorly placed dorsal and anal fins typical of salmonoids they lack the characteristic adipose fin. They also lack several bones in the skull. Superficially, they resemble the noodle fish but have particular features of the paired fin girdles and gill arches which make them unique. They are the smallest of all salmonoid species, one of them becoming mature at 0.5in (1.5cm) long. If such a phenomenon were possible, they are "even more" neotenic than the Salangidae.

The **argentines** (their name reflecting their silvery sheen, not their geographical distribution) are completely marine salmonoids. Also called herring smelts they reveal their osmeroid relationships by having an adipose fin and by superficially resembling the anadromous freshwater osmerid smelts. They are mostly small, usually less than 12in (30cm). They are elongate, slender, silvery fish, darker on the back, usually lacking distinctive markings or coloration. They have scales, a well-developed, rather flag-like dorsal fin high on the back, usually in front of the ventral fins, which are in the abdominal region. The head is longish with a pointed snout, the mouth small and terminal. The eyes are very large, a common feature of fish living at some depth in the sea. Although not well known, argentines are widespread in most oceans of the world; they are found down to about 3,300ft (1,000m), mostly a few hundred yards down, where they probably live in aggregations, if not in coordinated schools. From their teeth and stomach contents we know that they are carnivores, living on small crustaceans, worms and other prey. Their small size and the depths at which they occur mean that they are not of prime importance to commercial fisheries, but are taken for processing. They also have a role as a forage fish for larger and more economically useful food fish of deep waters.

Although the adults are deepwater fish, the eggs and young are found in the surface waters of the ocean, usually over the continental shelf. Their eggs are 0.1in (3–3.5mm) in diameter. They are slow-growing fish, and long lived, one estimate being that they may live for 20 years or more.

There are several genera, *Argentina* and *Glossanodon* being the typical argentinids, whereas *Microstoma* and *Nansenia* are greatly elongated species and *Xenophthalmichthys* is bizarre with tubular eyes that look forwards like a pair of automobile headlights.

The family Bathylagidae is divided into two superficially very different groups. The group that gives its name to the family consists of small, dark, large-eyed fishes found worldwide at depths of about 11,500ft (3,500m) or less. Nothing is known of their biology beyond the fact that some species eat crustaceans.

The other group, the opisthoproctids, is altogether more remarkable. There are six genera and probably about a dozen species in tropical and temperate seas down to about 3,300ft (1,000m). All of the species have tubular eyes. In the deep-bodied species (*Opisthoproctus*, *Macropinna* and *Winteria*) the eyes point directly upwards. In the fragile, slender-bodied forms (*Dolichopteryx* and *Bathylynchnops*) the eyes point forwards. The remaining species (*Rhychnohyalus natalensis*), which is known from only three examples, is alleged to be intermediate.

Opisthoproctus grimaldii grows to about 4in (10cm) long and lives in the North Atlantic. Its body is silvery, with a scattering of dark spots on the back. The sides of the body are covered with very deep scales. A swim bladder is present. The skull is so transparent that in live or freshly dead specimens the brain can be seen clearly behind the eyes. The spherical lenses in the tubular eyes are pale green. The ventral edge of the body is flattened and expanded into a shallow trough known as the sole. The base of the sole is silvery but covered with large thin scales and a dark pigment. The sole is believed to act as a reflector for the light produced by bacteria in a gland near the anus. The light from the gland passes through a lens and is then reflected downwards by a light-guide chamber just above the flattened part.

Opisthoproctus soleatus, a widespread species, has a different pigmentation pattern on the sole from its only congener, so it is thought that the sole enables species recognition in the areas where the two species live together. The upward pointing, tubular eyes, which afford excellent binocular vision, would easily be able to perceive the light directed downwards. The main food of the North Atlantic species (*O. grimaldii*) seems to be small, jellyfish-like organisms.

Dolichopteryx longipes is slender and very fragile. It is also very rare. The fins are elongated like a filament and there is no swim bladder. The muscles are very poorly developed; indeed, it has lost so much of its ventral musculature that the gut is enclosed only by transparent skin. It is, therefore, probably a very poor swimmer, and the tubular eyes may be advantageous in avoiding predators. Unlike *Opisthoproctus*, there is a light-producing organ associated with the eye. The species has been caught, infrequently, in all tropical and subtropical oceans between 1,150 and 8,860ft (350–2,700m) deep.

The family Bathyprionidae is based on fewer than six examples of its only species *Bathyprion danae*. It is a pike-like fish, living at depths of some 8,200ft (2,500m) in the South Indian Ocean and the North and Southeast Atlantic. It probably hovers waiting for very small fishes or crustaceans to come close when, so its fin positions would suggest, it surges forward to grab the prey.

Neither they, nor their close relatives the Alepocephalidae, have an adipose fin. The latter family are called **slickheads** because the head is covered with a smooth skin whereas the body has large scales. Most species are dark brown, violet or black in color. Light organs are rare among slickheads, but one genus, *Xenodermichthys*, is distinguished by the presence of tiny, raised light organs on the underside of the head and body.

The members of the remaining family in this assemblage, the Searsiidae, are deep-sea fishes with large, extremely light-sensitive eyes. The lateral-line canals on the head are greatly enlarged and expanded. They are found in all except polar waters and the family is characterized by a unique light organ on the shoulder above the pectoral fin. Light-producing cells are contained in a dark sac which opens to the outside by a backwards-pointing pore. When the fish is alarmed, a bright cloud is squirted out which lasts a few seconds and enables it to escape into the darkness.

A living example of the genus *Searsia* "was seen to discharge a bright luminous cloud into the water on being handled. The light appeared as multitudinous bright points, blue-green in color." There are also series of stripelike or rounded luminous organs underneath the body.   RMcD/KEB

◄▲► **Representative members of the order Salmoniformes.** (1) *Xenophthalmichthys danae*, a slender deep-water species of the family of Argentines or herring smelts (5in, 12cm). (2) Two views of *Opisthoproctus grimaldii*, a small deep-sea member of the family Salmonidae with upward-pointing tubular eyes (2in, 6cm). (3) A charr (genus *Salvelinus*), of the family Salmonidae (3ft, 90cm). (4) The ayu (*Plecoglossus altivelis*), sole species of its family (10in, 25cm). (5) *Prototroctes oxyrhynchus*, the New Zealand species of the family of southern graylings, now presumed to be extinct (12in, 30cm). (6) The Alaskan blackfish (*Dallia pectoralis*), a species of the family of mudminnows (8in, 20cm), (7) A fish of the genus *Aulostomatomorpha*, a long-snouted member of the family of slickheads from the Indian Ocean (6in, 15cm). (8) A species of the genus *Searsia* (family Searsiidae) squirting liquid to form a luminescent cloud (6in, 15cm).

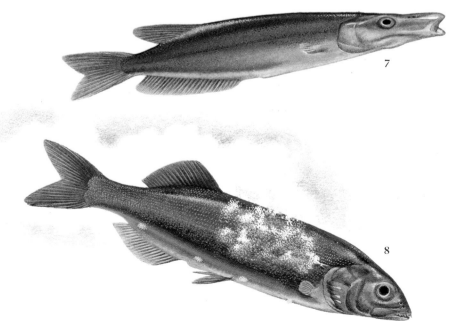

BRISTLE MOUTHS AND ALLIES

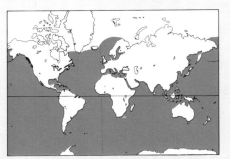

Size: maximum adult length 14in (35cm); most are much smaller.

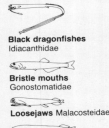

Black dragonfishes
Idiacanthidae

Bristle mouths
Gonostomatidae

Loosejaws Malacosteidae

Scaleless black dragonfishes
Melanostomidae

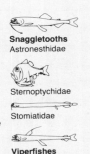

Snaggletooths
Astronesthidae

Sternoptychidae

Stomiatidae

Viperfishes
Chauliodontidae

LUMINOUS organs, bristle-like teeth, eyes on stalks—these are some of the characteristics of the order Stomiiformes, a worldwide group of deep-sea fishes contained in nine families. The classification of the order is very uncertain and the subject of active research, hence some of the families included here may well be transferred to other orders.

Practically all stomiiform species have luminous organs and many also have a luminous chin barbel, thought to act as a lure. They are flesh-eating fishes with a large, wide-gaping, toothed mouth. Most are scaleless, black or dark brown in color, but one family in particular—the Gonostomatidae—are mostly silvery, midwater fishes. Typically an adipose fin is present, but this and the pectoral and dorsal fins have been lost in some lineages.

The Gonostomatidae are known as bristle mouths because of their fine, bristle-like teeth. The genus *Cyclothone*, with over 20 species, occurs in all oceans. It is probably the commonest genus in the world regarding numbers of individuals: trawls can haul up tens of thousands of these small fish at a time. They feed on small crustaceans and other small invertebrates, and in turn are a most important source of food for larger fishes, including some of their relatives.

The maximum size of a particular stomiiform species depends upon the richness of the environment. In areas of abundance, such as the Bay of Bengal and the Arabian Sea, the species may reach 2.5in (6cm) long, but in a polluted area, like the depths of the Mediterranean, or in an area poor in food they are much smaller. The Mediterranean species *Cyclothone pygmaea* grows to only 1in (2.5cm).

Some species occur worldwide whereas others have a very limited distribution. As well as a two-dimensional distribution that can be shown on a map there is also a three-dimensional distribution as species are separated vertically. Generally, silvery or transparent species live nearer the surface than the dark-colored species. It is also generally true that the species living deeper have weaker and fewer light organs than those living above them. The swim bladder is poorly developed, which may explain why they do not undertake the extensive daily vertical migrations common in many deep-sea fishes.

Cyclothone species show differences between the sexes not with different light-organ patterns, as in the lantern fish, but in the nature of the nasal complex. In males, as they mature, the olfactory organs grow out through the nostrils. In some species, eg *Cyclothone microdon*, the hydrodynamic disadvantage of the protruding nasal plates (lamellae) is thought to be compensated for by the development of an elongate rostrum.

The Idiacanthidae is a family of elongated, scaleless fishes also lacking a swim bladder. Worldwide in distribution, the number of species is uncertain; there may be less than half a dozen or just one variable species.

The North Atlantic species *Idiacanthus fasciola* is remarkable for extreme differences between the sexes and its most peculiar larvae. The sex of the larvae cannot be determined until they are about 1.5in (4cm) long. They are, however, so peculiar that they were assigned to a separate genus (*Stylophthalmus*) until it was realized that they were the young of *Idiacanthus*. They are stalk-eyed, ie the eyes are at the end of cartilaginous rods which extend up to one-third of the body length. The body is transparent, the intestine extends beyond the tail and the pelvic fins are not developed. However, the pectoral fins (lost in the adult) are well developed. The larva lacks luminous organs.

During metamorphosis the eye stalks gradually shorten until the eyes rest in an orthodox position in the orbit of the skull. The pectoral fins are lost and only the female

develops pelvic fins. She also grows a luminous chin barbel, develops rows of small luminous organs on the body and strong jaws with thin, hooked teeth. The male never has a barbel nor teeth but develops a large luminous organ just below the eye. The female is black, the male brown. The male does not grow after metamorphosis so remains less than 2in (5cm) long, whereas the female feeds actively on prey of suitable size and can grow to over 12in (30cm) long.

The general biology of *Idiacanthus* is poorly known. The smallest larvae are caught at the greatest depths and metamorphosing larvae at about 1,000ft (300m), so they probably spawn at considerable depths. As the catches of larvae are sporadic it has been thought that they may shoal or otherwise agglomerate. The adults undergo a daily vertical migration from 6,000ft (1,800m) deep during the day to reach the surface at night.

The family Chauliodontidae contains about six species in the one genus *Chauliodus*. These are mid-water fishes distributed worldwide in oceans between 60 degrees N and 40 degrees S. *Chauliodus sloani* has been recorded from all oceans, but distinct and discrete populations have been recognized by some authors. "From all oceans" does not necessarily mean that the species is equally and universally distributed within the stated range. Oceans consist of distinct water masses varying in temperature, salinity, current, food supplies, etc. The way that fish are distributed within these water masses is exemplified by the distribution of *Chauliodus* species.

Two small species of *Chauliodus*, *C. danae* and *C. minimus*, live respectively in the central water masses of the North and South Atlantic. A larger species, *C. sloani*, lives in the richer waters that flow around the poorer central water masses. *Chauliodus sloani* grows to over 1ft (30cm) long, more than twice the length of the central-water species. Even the oxygen content of water can limit a distribution: *Chauliodus pammelas* lives only in the deep waters off Arabia which have a low oxygen content. To cope with these conditions it has gill filaments much longer than those of its congeners.

Chauliodus species are highly specialized predators. The second ray of their dorsal fin is elongated, highly mobile, and has a luminous lure at the end. Their teeth vary in shape within the mouth but this variation is remarkably consistent throughout each species. The front teeth on the upper jaw have four sharp ridges near the tip and are used for stabbing. The longest teeth (which

▲ **Denizen of the depths,** the head of a deep-sea fish (genus *Chauliodus*).

◄ **The fine teeth** clearly seen on the jaws of this *Gonostoma atlantica* are the feature of the family Gonostomatidae from which their common name bristle mouths is derived.

▼ ► **Loosejaws** have remarkably distensible jaws. (The species BELOW is *Malacosteus niger*.)

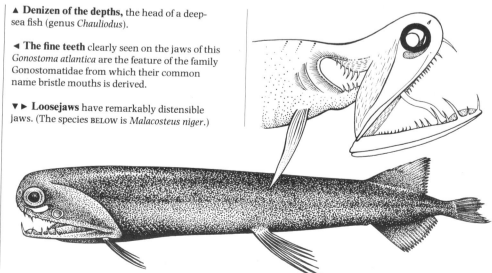

imply a remarkable gape) are the front two on the lower jaw. Normally when the mouth is closed they lie outside the upper jaw, but when they impale the prey their natural curvature tends to push the prey into the roof of the mouth. At the base of both the second and third upper jaw teeth there is a small tooth sticking out sideways which is thought to protect the large luminous organ below the eye.

These specialized, predatory modifications do not end with the teeth. The heart, ventral aorta and gill filaments are all much further forwards than is usual—in fact they lie between the sides of the lower jaw, the gill filaments extending almost to the front of it. Bearing in mind the fragility and importance of the gill filaments, how does large prey pass through the mouth without damaging them? The answer lies in the backbone. In almost all fish this consists of a series of firmly articulated bones which allow normal flexibility. In Chauliodus the front vertebrae generally do not develop and the spinal column remains a flexible cartilaginous rod. Although this is normal in embryonic and juvenile states (the notochord) bony vertebrae generally replace it in adults. However, its retention in Chauliodus enables the head to enjoy a remarkable freedom of movement. As the back muscles pull the head upwards, the hinge between the upper and lower jaws is pushed forwards. At the same time the mouth is opened, and the shoulder girdle, to which the heart is attached, is pulled backwards

and downwards. Special muscles pull the gill arches and their filaments downwards, away from the path of the prey. Movable teeth in the throat then clutch the prey and slowly transfer it to the elastic stomach. With the prey stowed away, these organs return to normal.

Chauliodus has been seen alive from a deep-sea submersible. It hangs still in the water, head lower than tail, with the long dorsal fin ray curved forwards to lie just in front of the mouth. The body is covered with a thick, watery sheath enclosed by a thin epidermis. This gelatinous layer is thickest dorsally and ventrally and thinnest laterally. It contains nerves, blood vessels and many small luminous organs.

Ignoring the lure, Chauliodus species have various kinds of luminescent organs (photophores). Along the ventral part of the fish are complex organs with two kinds of secretory cells, a pigment layer and a reflector. This type of organ is specialized below the eye, protected by teeth and transparent bones, with pigment layers and reflectors so arranged that the light shines into the eye. It is believed that this makes the eye more sensitive to light. Small light organs above and in front of the eye are thought to illuminate possible prey, suggesting that sight is an important factor in feeding. Scattered throughout the gelatinous sheath and inside the mouth are small, simple photophores which in life emit a bluish light. These are spherical and their bioluminous product is secreted into the hollow center of

▲ **Obscured by light.** Deep sea hatchet fishes have ventrally directed luminous organs which help to prevent them being seen by a predator below.

▼ **Fashioned by depth.** Species of the deep-sea fish family Stomiatidae live in all tropical oceans down to 4,600ft (1,400m). Larger species normally live at greater depths than smaller ones.

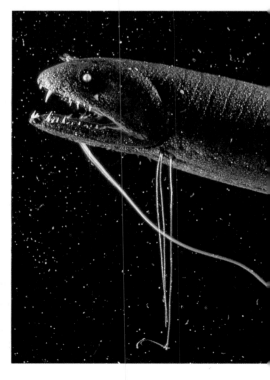

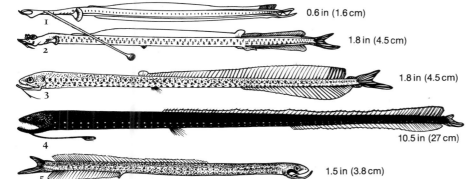

0.6 in (1.6 cm)

1.8 in (4.5 cm)

1.8 in (4.5 cm)

10.5 in (27 cm)

1.5 in (3.8 cm)

▲ **An awesome orifice.** TOP With its large teeth and luminous chin barbels *Stomias boa* displays the typical characteristics of the family of scaled dragon fishes.

▲ **The extraordinary development** of *Idiacanthus fasciola*. (1) A sexually indeterminate larva. (2) A post-larval female. (3) An adolescent female. (4) An adult female. (5) An adult male. Note the eye-stalk of the juvenile and the very different appearance of the adult male and female.

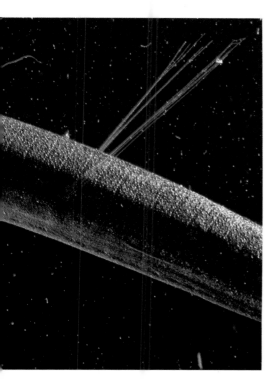

the organ. They are controlled by nerves, unlike the ventral luminous organs, and their function is unknown, but some interesting observations have been made.

When a *Chauliodus* is tranquil its ventral organs produce a bluish light. When touched, pulses of light illuminate the whole body. On top of this it has been demonstrated in an experiment that the intensity of the ventral photophores can be adjusted to match the amount of light received by the fish from above. In the clearest parts of the oceans all traces of sunlight have been absorbed at about 3,000ft (900m). Fishes below that depth lack ventral photopores. *Chauliodus* lives higher so is therefore affected by low light levels. The photophore by the eye varies its intensity with that of the ventral photophores and presumably, by balancing internal and external light levels, *Chauliodus* can produce the correct level of light from its ventral photophores to match the background illumination, thus making itself less liable to predation from below.

Species of *Malacosteus*, a black-skinned genus of the family Malacosteidae, are known as loosejaws. They have no floor to the mouth and the stark jaws with their long teeth are reminiscent of the cruel efficiency of gin traps. Some species in this family are unusual in that they have a cheek light organ producing a red light. Most photophores produce a blue-green light.

The species of the family Melanostomidae are called scaleless black dragon fish. They

live in all oceans and are predators. Some species are elongated whilst others are squatter. All have dorsal and anal fins set far back and large, fang-like teeth and rows of small, ventral, luminous organs. Almost all species have chin barbels which can vary from the very small, through multibranched versions, to ones six times the length of the body.

In the family Sternoptychidae species are laterally compressed and deep-chested, so are known as deep-sea hatchet fishes. Some have tubular eyes and in many the mouth is vertical. Species in the genus *Argyropelecus* have upwardly directed tubular eyes with a yellow, spherical lens. They feed on very small crustaceans. Some species undergo a small daily vertical migration. The genus *Polyipnus* has about 20 species, mostly in the western Pacific. All stay close to land at depths of 150–1,500ft (45–450m). Like all members of this family they have large, elaborate, downwardly pointing light organs. The photophores of species in the genus *Sternoptyx* have been studied intensively. They have two elliptical patches on the roof of the mouth which lack pigment, reflectors, or colored filters. They luminesce independently of the ventral organs and can glow for about half an hour before gently fading. Apart from, presumably, attracting prey there is a sort of light guide that allows some of this light to be guided close to the eye, where it may be used to relate the light production from the ventral organs to match the background daylight. The sternoptychids are exceedingly beautiful silvery fishes, though what advantage their hatchet shape gives them is unknown. *Maurolicus muelleri*, a small, sprat-like fish often found at night at the surface of the North Atlantic, is thought to be a primitive relative of the deep-sea hatchet fishes. It resembles them in many internal details but has a more normal fish shape.

Members of the family that has given its name to the order—the Stomiidae—are known as the scaled dragon fishes. There are only two genera, *Stomias* with eight species and *Macrostomias* with one. Elongated predators, lacking an adipose fin, they are found in the Indo-Pacific and Atlantic Oceans. They have large, easily shed, hexagonal scales that produce a pleasing honeycomb pattern on their dark bodies. *Stomias* species lack a swim bladder, so they can easily undertake extensive daily vertical migrations. There are usually two rows of small light organs along the ventral margin of the body. At their longest the scaled dragon fishes rarely exceed 12in (30cm).   KEB

Light from Living Organisms

How fish produce and use artificial illumination

As a terrestrial creature who in his waking hours is accustomed to light, man has little appreciation of life-styles that must cope with continual darkness. Yet that is precisely what life would be like in the world's oceans were it not for bioluminescence, the production of light by living organisms. Not to be confused with phosphorescence or fluorescence, light that results from the excited state of inanimate crystals, bioluminescence is the result of the chemical reaction of a substance, usually luciferin, and an enzyme, a luciferase, which is controlled by a living organism. Bioluminescence also occurs on land—it is best known from fireflies in an evening sky or glowing fungi on a forest floor; it does not occur in freshwater fishes, but its greatest display in variety and intensity occurs in the sea.

Of the nearly 20,000 living species of fishes, perhaps 1,000–1,500 bioluminesce. None of the lampreys and hagfishes or lungfishes are known to, but six genera of midwater and benthic sharks and species representing nearly 190 genera of marine bony fishes are luminescent. This is best seen in the lantern fishes, the gonostomatids, the families of dragonfishes (Melanostomiatidae, Malacosteidae, Chauliodontidae, etc), the slickheads (Alepocephalidae and Searsiidae) and the angler fishes (various families). Several shallow-water and bottom-living fish families also contain luminescent species, and these are better understood behaviorally and physiologically in that they are amenable to capture and study. Included are the ponyfishes (Leiognathidae), flashlight fishes (Anomalopidae), pinecone fishes (Monocentridae), midshipman fishes (Batrachoididae), and several of the cardinal fishes (Apogonidae).

The origin of the light and the associated chemistry may be conveniently divided into two categories. The first are those with self-luminous photophores—specialized structures usually arranged in rows and consisting of highly complex lenses, reflectors and pigmented screens. The skin photophores produce light by the photogenic cells and reflect it through the lens and cornea-like epidermis. The more than 840 photophores in the belly of the California midshipman (*Porichthys notatus*) produce a gentle, even glow whose intensity can be slowly modulated to match the downwelling moonlight upon the sandy bottom. The second category involves luminous bacterial symbionts, maintained in complex organs and nurtured by the host fish in exchange for a more brilliant level of light. This extrinsic form of light production does not allow the fish to control the bacterial light which continues to effuse, therefore the hosts have evolved fascinating mechanisms to turn out their lights when they would be a hindrance.

▶ **A complex luminous organ** (photophore) ABOVE from a deep-sea hatchet fish (genus *Argyropelecus*). A common pattern is shown here. The light-producing organs are partly screened by pigment cells and backed by a reflective layer which directs the light to the lens, in some cases through filters to change the color of the light emission.

▶ **Light in the shallows.** The Flashlight fish (belonging to the order Beryciformes of spiny-finned fishes) is one of the few shallow-water luminous fishes. It has a large light organ below the eye which flashes on and off. Only recently have public aquaria learned how to keep these fish so that all can see the beauty of their natural light, though they have not yet been bred in captivity. The light is produced by bacteria housed in cells well provided with blood vessels. The function of the organ is uncertain, but in parts of the eastern Indian Ocean it is used by native fishermen as a bait.

▶ **The strings of beads** FAR RIGHT on the underside of this fish (*Valenciennellus tripunctatus*, of the superorder of bristle mouths and allies) are its luminescent organs. Each organ is a highly complex structure.

▼ **Photophores in profusion,** a deepsea viperfish photographed under ultraviolet light (*Chauliodus sloani*, of the superorder of bristle mouths and allies).

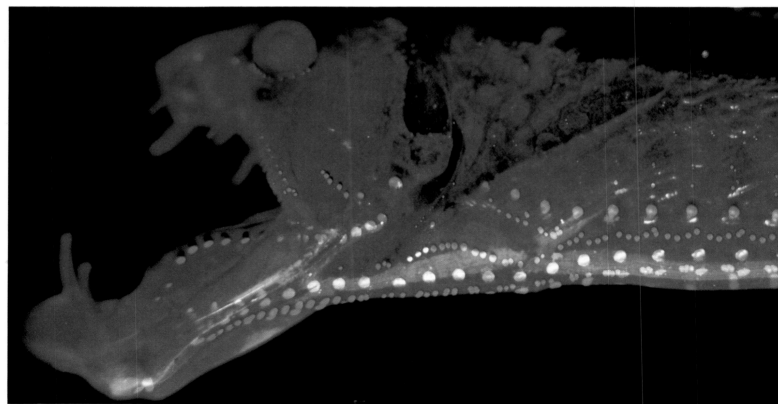

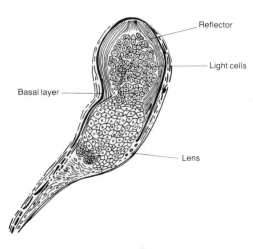

Reflector

Light cells

Basal layer

Lens

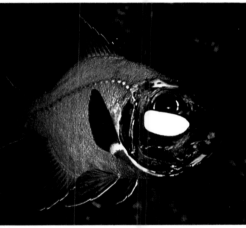

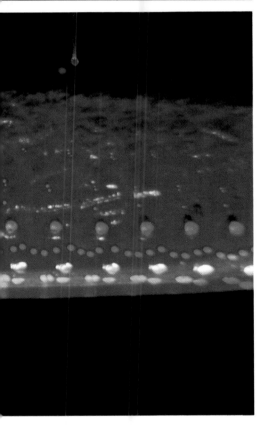

What then is the function of bioluminescence for fishes? In the case of most deepsea fishes it is one of camouflage through counter-illumination. Even at 3,300ft (1,000m) in clear tropical waters, downwelling light would silhouette a lanternfish to an upward-searching predator were it not for the weak glow of the rows of photophores on its underside which cancel its apparent presence. Other photophores on its body can be used as well to advertise its species and its sex. The large suborbital light organs of *Aristostomias*, *Pachystomias* and *Malacosteus* emit red light which, when coupled with its red-sensitive retina, might act like a "snooperscope" to hunt prey that can only see blue-green hues. Other uses in the deepsea include luring, as has been achieved by many melanostomiatid dragon fishes with elongate luminous chin barbels or angler fishes with luminous escas at the end of their modified first dorsal spine. Concealment is also a function whereby slickheads and certain macrourids presumably behave like squids and octopuses, leaving a predator snapping at a luminous ink cloud.

The behavior and bioluminescent function of shallow-water fishes is becoming better understood as a result of foolhardy nocturnal observers with scuba gear and the improvement in aquarium collecting and husbandry. The pine-cone fishes (*Monocentris japonicus* and *Cleidopus gloriamaris*) live in shallow water and apparently lure nocturnal crustacean prey to their jaws with the light organs located in their mouth and on their jaws. Bioluminescence is best perfected in the anomalopid flashlight fishes. These small, black reef associates possess an immense subocular light organ, capable of emitting enough light to be seen from 100ft (30m) away. In evening twilight they migrate up from deep water to feed along the reef edge and return before daylight to the recesses of the deep reef. They use the light for a multiplicity of purposes, including finding food, attracting food, communication and avoiding predators. Flashlight fishes continually blink, either by raising a black eyelid-like structure or by rotating the entire organ into a dark pocket. The living light produced by the flashlight fish *Photoblepharon palpebratus* is the most intense yet discovered.

This brief summary of fish bioluminescence reflects the meager knowledge man has of life in the nocturnal sea. As our ability to descend into the deep ocean at night improves, many more forms of extraordinary behavior associated with bioluminescence will surely come to light.   JEM

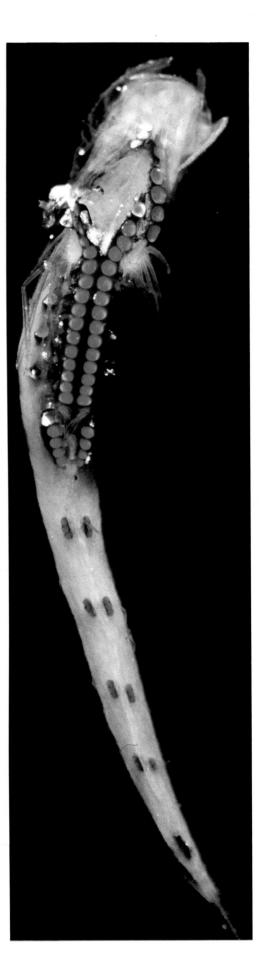

LIZARD FISHES, LANTERN FISHES

Orders: Aulopiformes, Myctophiformes
About four hundred and forty species in about
75 genera and about 13 families.

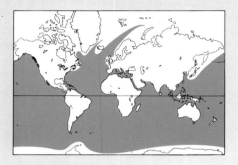

Lizard fishes and allies or aulopoids
Order: Aulopiformes
About one hundred and ninety species in about
40 genera and 11 or 12 families.
Distribution: all oceans.
Size: maximum length 6.5ft (2m).
Families, genera and species include:
Aulopidae, including **Sergeant Baker** (*Aulopus
purpurissimus*); **barracudinas** (family
Paralepididae); Bathypteroidae, including
tripod fishes (genus *Bathypterois*); **Bombay
ducks** (family Harpadontidae);
chlorophthalmids (family Chlorophthalmidae);
giganturoids (family Giganturidae); **lancet fish**
(family Alepisauridae); **lizard fishes** (family
Synodontidae).

Lantern fishes
Order: Myctophiformes
About two hundred and fifty to three hundred
species in 35 genera and 2 families.
Distribution: deeper water of all oceans.
Size: maximum length 12in (30cm).

Lizard fishes

Aulopidae

Giganturoids Giganturidae

Lizard fishes Synodontidae

Ipnopidae

Lantern fishes

Barracudinas Paralepididae

Lancet fishes Alepisauridae

Bathypteroidae

Lantern fishes Myctophidae

Neoscopelidae

Bombay ducks
Harpadontidae

Omosudidae

Chlorophthalmids
Chlorophthalmidae

Pearleyes Scopelarchidae

Daggertooth
Anotopteridae

Sabertooth fishes
Evermannellidae

VARIOUS extraordinary fishes belong to
the two orders of lizard fishes and lantern fishes: tripod fishes, which sit on their
stiffened pelvic fins and lower tail lobe; species in the genus *Ipnops*, which have greatly
flattened eyes covering the top of the skull;
the lantern fishes, speckled with luminous
organs; that famous delicacy the Bombay
duck; and others.

The 14 or so families in these two closely
related orders were formerly considered by
some authorities to be more realistically
included in one order. The arrangement
here follows the latest classification in which
just two families, Myctophidae and
Neoscopelidae, comprise the Myctophiformes; all the others are Aulopiformes.

Within the order of **lizard fishes** and allies
the number of families is uncertain, and one
of the reasons for this stems from the deep-
sea tripod fishes. They have been photographed on the deep-sea floor resting on
their stiffened pelvic fins and the lower lobe
of the tail, facing into the current with their
bat-like pectoral fins raised over the head in
the manner of forward-pointing elk horns.
The 18 or so species of tripod fish are found
worldwide in deep water. However, they are
only found in a particular type of oceanic
water mass called central oceanic water.
Formerly they were grouped in the genera
Bathysauropsis, *Bathytyphlops*, *Bathymicrops*
and *Bathypterois*, all placed in the family
Bathypteroidae. Recent research has shown
that they should all be included in one
genus, *Bathypterois*. It was known that their
family was related to two others, the
Chlorophthalmidae and the Ipnopidae
(which contains just one genus of most
peculiar deep-sea fishes). Further research
placed this assemblage in perspective with
the rest of the aulopoids and the conclusion
was reached that they are all more closely
related to each other than to the rest of
the aulopoids, hence they are now just one
family—the Chlorophthalmidae—not three.
As not all workers agree with this the result
is vague statements on the number of families present in the order.

Each species of tripod fish lives only in
a particular area, defined by subtle
parameters of temperature and salinity.
Bathypterois atricolor may occur in waters as
shallow as 1,000ft (300m) whereas
B. longicauda lives as deep as 19,700ft
(6,000m); *B. filiferus* lives only off South
Africa whereas *B. longipes* is circumglobal.
All, however, can only live where the sea
floor is composed of ooze or very fine sand
which permits a firm "foothold" for their
fins. One puzzle is that there are large areas

of deep sea, eg the North Pacific, with ideal
conditions (as far as can be seen) in which
they do not live. For deep-sea fish they are
common. Off the Bahamas intensive surveys
have shown there can be almost 233 fish per
sq mi (90 per sq km). The bat-like pectoral
fins have an elaborate nerve supply, so are
sensory, but for what use is not known. The
eyes are extremely small. The fish feed on
small crustaceans which we can but
presume are detected by the fins as they drift
past in the current. There is so much that
remains unknown, including the life history
of these fish.

Fish in the genus *Ipnops*, with 3 or 4 species, look a bit like a flattened tripod fish without the tripod. They appear to be eyeless. They have achieved fame because of the puzzle presented, since they were first discovered, by the two large, flat, pale yellow plates on the top of the head. For about half a century it was thought that they were luminous organs that directed light upwards. The advent of deep-sea photography revealed that these plates were highly reflective. The flash from a deep-sea camera that photographed one was clearly reflected from the plates.

In the last few years deep-sea collecting has made more specimens available to scientists and the puzzle of the plates has been solved: they are a mixture of modified eyes and skull bones. Each plate, which covers half of the head width, is a transparent skull bone. The reflective layer below this is a very much changed eye retina. Ordinary eye structures, like the lens, have been lost; only the light-sensitive retina remains and this has been spread out over the top of the head and is protected by the skull. Although this is remarkable, it is difficult to understand what it means to the fish. It can

▼ **Wide-eyed repose.** This species of lizard fish (*Saurida gracilis*) from the Great Barrier Reef shows the typical observant resting position.

detect light coming down from above, yet it cannot focus on an object. Furthermore, it eats marine worms which live below it.

The chlorophthalmids are the orthodox members of the family. They are laterally compressed, silvery fishes with large eyes. They grow up to 12in (30cm) long, have dorsal and ventral fins well forward and an adipose fin directly above the anal fin. *Chlorophthalmus* species are widespread and fairly abundant in the North Atlantic, where they shoal at depths of 660 to 2,460ft (200–750m). In all species the lateral line system is well developed and greatly expanded into special organs on the snout, head and gill covers. These organs enable the fish to detect the approach of small prey.

The dim light from the perianal organ (an organ around the anus) is produced by bacteria. The presence of this light is believed to enable a fish to maintain contact with its fellows and perhaps to facilitate mating opportunities among those in breeding condition. The scientific name for the family comes from the green light reflected by the tapetum (a reflective layer behind the eye) in some species. Yellow eye lenses are common; the yellow coloring is believed to act as a selective filter enabling the fish to "see through" the downwardly directed luminous camouflage emanating from the ventral light organs of the small crustaceans that form its prey.

Only three families in this group are shallow- or moderately shallow-water fishes, the Aulopidae, the lizard fishes and the Bombay ducks. The last family is famous in Indian restaurants as the crispy, salty delicacy (the aforementioned Bombay duck) eaten before the meal. What you are eating is the sun-dried, salted fillet of a large-mouthed, large-toothed fish from the Ganges estuary. Its slender, cylindrical body with a soft dorsal fin and an adipose fin is typical of many aulopoids. Almost all are predatory, using their curved needle-like teeth to seize fish and invertebrates. The members of the other major shallow-sea family, the lizard fishes, are bottom dwellers, spending time propped up on their pectoral fins waiting for dinner to swim by. They get their common name not just from the very lizard-like shape of the head but also from their rapid feeding movements. Both these families live in warm waters.

The lancet fish are large, voracious, midwater predators. None have luminous organs but all have large stabbing teeth and distensible stomachs. Species in the genus *Alepisaurus* can reach 6ft (1.8m) in length but their bodies are so slender that a fish of this size will only weigh 4–5lb (1.8–2.3kg). They have a small anal fin and a very long, very high dorsal fin that can be folded down into a deep groove along the back and become invisible. The function of this large dorsal fin is unknown but it has been suggested that it might be used like the similarly large dorsal fin of the sail fishes in helping to "round up" shoals of small fishes. The diet of the Atlantic lancet fish *Alepisaurus ferox* consists of deep-sea hatchet fish, barracudinas, squids, octopi and almost anything else available. Most of the fish eaten do not undertake daytime migrations. Lantern fish, although abundant, are rarely eaten and it is thought that a result of their daily migration is to avoid predation by lancet fish. Lancet fish are, however, eagerly eaten by tunas and other surface predators when the opportunity arises.

The scaleless body of the Pacific lancet fish is dark gray to greenish dorsally, silvery on the sides, somewhat iridescent with pale spots. The large dorsal fin is black or dark blue/gray with steely blue reflections. The pectoral, caudal and adipose fins are dark, the others paler.

Anotopterus pharao lacks the large dorsal fin of *Alepisaurus* but has a similarly shaped body. This species, which lives in cool polar waters, is sometimes placed in its own family, the Anotopteridae.

A 30in (75cm) long, intact specimen of *Anotopterus pharao*, taken from the stomach of a whale in the Antarctic, was found to have two barracudinas, 11 and 7in (27 and 18cm) long, both engorged with krill, in its distensible stomach.

The barracudinas derive their common name from their superficial resemblance to the predatory barracudas of coral reefs to which they are not related. Barracudinas are slender fishes with large jaws, many small, sharp, pointed teeth on the upper jaw and a mixture of larger stabbing teeth on the lower. A small adipose fin is present and the single, soft-rayed dorsal fin is in the rear half of the body. Scales, when present, are fragile and easily shed. This is thought to be an adaptation towards the swallowing of large prey by permitting easier body expansion. The anus is often much closer to the pelvic fins than to the anal fin. In many species there is a fleshy keel between the anus and the anal fin.

The family is widespread but the range of individual species is more limited. *Notolepis coatsi*, a species growing to more than 4in (10cm) long, is confined to Antarctic waters. *Notolepis coruscans* comes from the eastern North Pacific. The barracudinas are

▲ **Fish of the warm seas,** TOP a lizard fish (genus *Synodus*) from Fiji.

▲ **Lizard in the heather,** ABOVE a lizard fish (genus *Synodus*) from the Great Barrier Reef.

▶ **Miniatures of the deep seas.** Most lantern fishes are small, between 1 and 6in (2.5–15cm). The light organs (photophores) are visible here as the small round dots.

unusual among the aulopoids in that they have light organs. In the genus *Lestidium* these consist of ducts that extend from the head to the ventral fins. The bacteria therein produce a bright, pale-yellow light. The function of the luminosity is unknown. It is probably not for camouflage because the species with luminous organs have an iridescent skin as well as being translucent. Perhaps the organs function as lighthouses enabling individuals of the same species to recognize one another.

The eyes of barracudinas are designed in such a way that their best field of binocular vision is directly downwards. However, barracudinas seen alive from submersibles oriented themselves head-up, or nearly so, in the water so that they were looking along a horizontal plane (ie straight ahead). It is also conjectured that the head-up posture presents a smaller silhouette for predators beneath them to spot.

The giganturoids are cylindrical, silvery fishes with forward-pointing tubular eyes set back on the snout, giving the fish the appearance of an old-fashioned racing car. Scales and luminous organs are absent. The pectoral fin is set high up on the body; the caudal fin has an elongated lower lobe; adipose and pelvic fins are missing. Also missing are a large number of bones. Indeed, the adult fish has been subjected to a loss of many features typically present in its relatives. Many of the remaining bones are still cartilaginous. The teeth are large, sharp and depressible to ease the passage of large prey. The inside of the mouth and stomach are lined with dense black pigment which, it has been suggested, blacks out the luminous organs of its last meal. The abdominal region is elastic so giganturoids can swallow food much larger than themselves. The pectoral fins are inserted above the level of the gills and are thought to help ventilate them during the slow passage of a large fish down the throat. Certainly some such device would have to be present as the normal water currents cannot flow through the blocked mouth to the gills.

Giganturoids are widespread in tropical and semitropical oceans at depths down to about 11,000ft (3.350m). All are small fishes, rarely exceeding 6in (15cm).

Members of the family Aulopidae, which has given its name to the order, are the most primitive aulopoids. They live in warm shallow waters in the Atlantic, parts of the Pacific and around southern coasts. They are scaled, bottom-living fishes with slender bodies and large heads. The second ray of the dorsal fin is characteristically elongate. An adipose fin is present. The teeth are small and lie in closely packed rows. Small, bottom-living invertebrates are the main food.

They are surprisingly colorful for fishes that live as far down as 3,000ft (915m); browns, reds and pinks are well represented among the dozen or so species. *Aulopus purpurissimus* is a highly colored, edible species from Australia. The edges of the scales are crimson against a purple or scarlet background. The fins are yellow with rows of red spots. Its common name of Sergeant Baker apocryphally alludes to the name of the soldier who first caught this fish in New South Wales. There is no evidence for this, but many red-colored fishes have a military common name in allusion to the red jackets of British troops.

The 300 or so species in the order Myctophiformes are commonly called **lantern fishes** because of the appearance created by their extensive speckling of luminous organs. These carnivorous fish live in the middle depths of all oceans and rarely exceed 1ft (30cm) long. The overall body shape is very similar in all species, but the pattern of light organs differs from species to species and is the basis for species definition. As well as the small photophores there are larger organs—upper and lower glands—mostly near the tail, which indicate the sex of the fish. Usually the female lacks the upper glands and the lower ones are less conspicuous or even absent. The fish react strongly to light signals. One animal being studied in an aquarium appeared to be most interested in the investigator's luminous wristwatch. Brighter light sources have little effect.

Lantern fishes live 1,000 to 2,300ft (300–700m) down. There are both silvery-bodied and dark-bodied forms. Many display an upward migration at night, occasionally to as little as 165ft (50m). Those with swim bladders have less fat than those without. Fat, being lighter than water, helps the latter maintain neutral buoyancy. Again to emphasize the theme that generalizations on fish are almost impossible, *Tarltonbeania crenularis* has no gas in its swim bladder, almost no fat and is negatively buoyant (ie is less dense than water). **KEB**

CHARACINS, CATFISHES, CARPS...

Superorder: Ostariophysi
About six thousand species in at least 907 genera and 50 families.
Distribution: worldwide, largely freshwater.

▲ **In want of lineage.** *Ellopostoma megalomycter* is known only from a handful of specimens. It has not yet been associated with any of the major cyprinoid families.

▶ **Dull fish in Africa.** There are fewer species of characins in Africa than in South America, and none has achieved the brilliant colors of some of the small Amazonian tetras. Africa's nearest approach to these popular aquarium fish is probably the Congo tetra (*Phenacogrammus interruptus*), shown here.

▼ **A sleek, silvery fish** BELOW RIGHT from the Indo-Pacific Ocean is the milk fish or bandang. It enters fresh water to spawn. A single fish can lay up to six million eggs.

▼ **Diagram of the Weberian mechanism,** seen from above, a characteristic feature of many members of the superorder Ostariophysi. It transmits vibrations from the swim bladder to the inner ear.

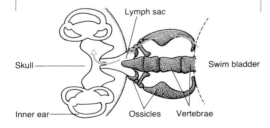

Lymph sac

Skull

Swim bladder

Inner ear

Ossicles   Vertebrae

CARPS, catfishes, characins, suckers, loaches and their allies are the dominant freshwater fishes in Eurasia and North America and arguably so in Africa and South America. (Only the catfishes are native to Australia.) The approximately 6,000 species are predominantly freshwater fish. Just two families of catfishes and one species of cyprinid are found at sea, although several genera may spend time in brackish water.

The major groups listed opposite are well defined (although their relationships are the subject of much controversy). However, one species, *Ellopostoma megalomycter* from Borneo, is a puzzle because it does not quite fit in anywhere.

The ostariophysi as a whole are split into two series, the otophysi and the anotophysi, the former having two hundred times more species than the latter. The otophysi have two main unifying characters. Firstly, the presence of an "alarm substance" secreted from glands in the skin when a fish is threatened, which causes a fright reaction in other otophysans. Perhaps understandably, the alarm substance is not present in families of heavily armored catfishes, but less comprehensible is its absence in some of the subterranean characins and cyprinids.

The second significant character is the Weberian mechanism. This is an elaborate modification of the first few vertebrae into a series of levers that transmit compression (ie sound) waves, received by the swim bladder, to the inner ear. Consequently, they have acute hearing. No one is certain how this complex "hearing aid" developed, but a clue may come from the anotophysi where there are "head ribs" that may be a primitive trial for such a mechanism.

The anotophysi are a diverse and somewhat incongruent group. The milk fishes are a genus of food fish from the region of Southeast Asia. They look rather like large herrings with small, silvery scales but lacking ventral scutes. They are intensively cultured in fish ponds in many areas and can grow to well over 3.3ft (1m) in length. They can tolerate a wide range of salinity.

Gonorhynchus gonorhynchus is the only member of its family (Gonorhynchidae). A shallow-water species from the temperate and tropical Indo-Pacific, it has an elongate body, long snout and a ventral mouth. There is no swim bladder. What could be fossil relatives have been found in Alberta, Canada.

Unlike *Gonorhynchus*, *Phractolaemus* from West African fresh waters has a dorsal mouth that extends like a short periscope. Its swim bladder is divided into small units and can be used for breathing atmospheric air. Growing to a little more than 6in (15cm) long, it is confined to the Niger and parts of the Zaïre basin.

The remaining anotophysan family is the Kneriidae, consisting of small freshwater fishes that feed on algae in tropical and nilotic African fresh waters. They exhibit marked sexual dimorphism whereby the male has a peculiar rosette, of unknown function, on its operculum. The genera *Cromeria* and *Grasseichthys* are neotenic, that is, they become sexually mature while still having a larval body form. By some authorities they are considered to be kneriids, by others they are placed in a separate family. These small, transparent fishes lack scales and a lateral line. They live in West African rivers.

The characins, catfishes and carps are a highly successful group and display a remarkable mixture of evolutionary conservatism and extreme radicalism which, when coupled with the plasticity or variability at the species level, makes their taxonomy very difficult. For such common fish, they are an enigmatic group.   KEB

The 4 Orders of Characins, Catfishes, Carps and Milk Fishes

Series: Otophysi

Characins
Order: Characiformes
Over one thousand two hundred species in over 250 genera and probably 10 families.

Distribution: fresh waters of Africa, South and Central America, and Southern North America.
Size: maximum length 5ft (1.5m).

Families, genera and species include: Characidae, including **tiger fishes** (genus *Hydrocynus*); **freshwater hatchet fishes** (family Gasteropelecidae); **glandulocaudines** (subfamily Glandulocaudinae); Lebiasinidae, including **Splashing tetra** (*Copella arnoldi*); Serrasalminae, including **piranhas** (genus *Serrasalmus*), **silver dollars** (genera *Metynis*, *Myleus*), **South American salmons** (genera *Catabasis*, *Salminus*), **wimple-piranhas** (genus *Catoprion*).

Catfishes
Order: Siluriformes
Over two thousand species in probably over 400 genera and 29 or 31 families.

Distribution: most habitable fresh waters; members of two families (Ariidae, Plotosidae) can inhabit tropical and subtropical seas.
Size: maximum length 10ft (3m).

Families, genera and species include: **amphiliids** (family Amphiliidae); **callichthyids** (family Callichthyidae); Clariidae, including **Walking catfish** (*Clarias batrachus*); **crucifix fish** (family Ariidae); Ictaluridae, including **blue** and **channel catfishes** and **bullheads** (genus *Ictalurus*), **flatheads** (genus *Pylodictis*), **madtoms** (genus *Noturus*); **loricariids** (family Loricariidae); **Parasitic catfishes** (family Trichomycteridae), including **candirus** (genera *Vandellia*, *Branchioca*); **pimelodids** (family Pimelodidae); **schilbeids** (family Schilbeidae); Siluridae, including **European wels** (*Silurus glanis*); **sisorids** (family Sisoridae).

Carps and allies or cyprinoids
Order: Cypriniformes
About two thousand five hundred species in over 250 genera and 6 or 7 families.

Distribution: North America, Europe, Africa, Asia almost exclusively in fresh water.
Size: maximum length 10ft (3m).

Families, genera and species include: cyprinids (family Cyprinidae), including **bighead carps** (genus *Hypophthalmichthys*), **bream** (genus *Abramis*), **carp** (*Cyprinus carpio*), **grass-carp** (genus *Ctenopharyngodon*), **mahseers** (genus *Barbus*), **roach** (genus *Rutilus*), **snow-trouts** (genus *Schizothorax*), **squawfish** (genus *Ptychocheilus*), **tench** (*Tinca tinca*), **yellow-cheek** (*Elopichthys bambusa*); **gyrinocheilids** (family Gyrinocheilidae); **Homalopterids** (family Homalopteridae); **loaches** (family Cobitidae), including **weather fish** (*Misgurnus fossilis*, *M. anguillicaudatus*); **psilorhynchids** (family Psilorhynchidae); **suckers** or **catostomids** (family Catostomidae).

Series: Anotophysi

Milk fishes and allies
Order: Gonorhynchiformes
About 30 species in 7 genera and 4 families.

Distribution: Indo-Pacific Ocean; fresh waters in tropical Africa.
Size: maximum length 6.5ft (2m).

Genera include: **milk fishes** (genus *Chanos*).

There are about 1,200 living species of **characins**, about 200 of which are found in Africa and the remainder in Central and South America. This discontinuous distribution implies that some 100 million years ago, characins were widespread in the area of the land mass Gondwanaland, which later split forming Africa and South America, Antarctica and Australia.

Superficially the characins resemble members of the carp family (cyprinids) but they usually have a fleshy adipose fin between the caudal and dorsal fins and have teeth on the jaws but not in the pharynx. In addition to their complete functional set of teeth characins also have a replacement set behind those in current use. In some species all the "old" teeth on one side of the upper and lower jaws drop out and the replacement ones take their place. Once these are firmly in position the teeth on the other side of the jaws are replaced. In predatory characins all the "old" teeth drop out and are rapidly replaced in one go. As soon as the replacement teeth are functional, new replacement teeth begin to grow in the tooth-replacement trenches.

There are five families of characin in Africa. They are both carnivorous and omnivorous, but are less varied and less interesting than the Neotropical species. The most primitive African characin is *Hepsetus odoe*, the sole member of the family Hepsetidae. It is a fish-eater of the lurking-predator type, with a large mouth provided with strong, conical teeth to prevent the prey's escape. Unusually for characiforms it lays eggs in a floating foam nest, which incidentally is considered a great gastronomic delicacy. On hatching, the larvae hang from the water surface by special adhesive organs on their heads.

Members of the family Ichthyboridae are elongate fishes that earn a living by snatching mouthfuls of scales and nipping notches out of the fins of other fishes. Their close relatives are a group of relatively harmless fishes belonging to the families Distichodontidae and Citharinidae. Their claim to fame is that they have scales with a serrated edge (ctenoid scales) unlike all other characins which have smooth (cycloid) scales. A few of these species are of local commercial importance.

The last family of African characins, Characidae (the characids), is shared with the Neotropics. There are only a few genera in Africa, but enormous numbers in Central and South America. The genus of African "tetras" (*Alestes*) is one of the best known groups of characids because of their

popularity with aquarists. They are fairly colorful fishes, often with a single lateral stripe and red, orange or yellow fins. The body can be short and deep or elongate (fusiform). All show sexual dimorphism in anal fin shape; in females the margin is completely straight but in males it is convex. These fish also show a curious sexual dimorphism in the caudal vertebrae. How they recognize it and what benefit it confers on them is unknown. The African tetras have very strong, multicusped teeth, for crushing and grinding their food of insects, fish and insect larvae, plankton and assorted vegetation.

The tiger fishes, a genus of close relatives of the African "tetras," have gained notoriety and their common name from their long, conical teeth which overlap the outside of the jaws when the mouth is shut and from their black body stripes (though these are horizontal rather than vertical). One Zaïrean species grows to over 5ft (1.5m) and weighs more than 100lb (45kg). There are a few unsubstantiated reports of tiger fish attacking people. They are, however, excellent sport fish, and generate an African equivalent of the excitement of catching a large salmon. Oddly, tiger fish lose all their "old" teeth at once so sometimes toothless individuals have been caught, but it only takes a matter of days for the replacement teeth to become functional.

The diversity in Neotropical characins ranges from voracious predators through tiny vegetarians to blind subterranean species. The piranhas are the most fabled

▲ **A change of style.** In Africa a characoid (*Hepsetus odoe*) has evolved the characteristics of a "lurking predator," that is the dorsal and anal fins are set far back near the tail to produce quick and powerful acceleration. In South America at least two genera have evolved in parallel to achieve the same end, including *Boulengerella maculata* shown here.

▶ **The much maligned piranha** has short, triangular teeth with sharp edges. It normally feeds on fishes and carrion in the wild. Observations in captivity suggest that the alleged "feeding frenzy" does not occur unless about 20 fish are gathered together.

▶ **One of the less spectacular characins** of South America BELOW is the Bleeding heart tetra (*Hyphessobrycon rubrostigma*). The contrasting colors on the dorsal fin are thought to be a "presence indicator" to keep the members of shoals together in dark waters.

▼ **Outlines of representative species** of characins, catfishes, carps and milk fishes.

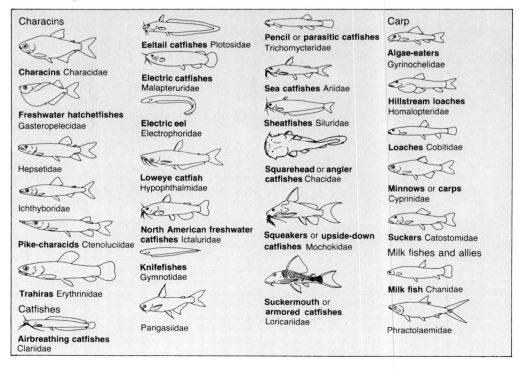

Characins

Characins Characidae

Freshwater hatchetfishes Gasteropelecidae

Hepsetidae

Ichthyboridae

Pike-characids Ctenoluciidae

Trahiras Erythrinidae

Catfishes

Airbreathing catfishes Clariidae

Eeltail catfishes Plotosidae

Electric catfishes Malapteruridae

Electric eel Electrophoridae

Loweye catfish Hypophthalmidae

North American freshwater catfishes Ictaluridae

Knifefishes Gymnotidae

Pangasiidae

Pencil or **parasitic catfishes** Trichomycteridae

Sea catfishes Ariidae

Sheatfishes Siluridae

Squarehead or **angler catfishes** Chacidae

Squeakers or **upside-down catfishes** Mochokidae

Suckermouth or **armored catfishes** Loricariidae

Carp

Algae-eaters Gyrinochelidae

Hillstream loaches Homalopteridae

Loaches Cobitidae

Minnows or **carps** Cyprinidae

Suckers Catostomidae

Milk fishes and allies

Milk fish Chanidae

Phractolaemidae

predatory fishes. They are stocky and rather ugly, having a deep head, short powerful jaws with triangular, interlocking, razor-sharp teeth. They are shoaling animals, and feed communally on smaller fish or allegedly on larger injured or supposedly healthy prey.

Of all the areas of fish lore the piranha legend is the least open to substantiation. Each piranha makes a clean bite of about 1 cubic in (16 cu cm) of flesh. Shoal size then dictates the speed with which the victim is despatched. In some areas the feeding frenzy is triggered by blood in the water and it takes only a few minutes for a victim to be reduced to little more than a skeleton. People wading or bathing in rivers have also been attacked. Legend has it that a man and horse fell into the water and were later found with all the flesh picked off, yet the man's clothes were found to be undamaged.

Piranhas are fairly small fishes, rarely exceeding 2ft (60cm), but are excellent sport fish. Anglers use a stout wire trace to catch them and they apparently make excellent eating. The piranhas' close relatives are the two vegetarian or omnivorous genera known to aquarists as silver dollars. Although they are similar in appearance, their nature is quite unlike that of the piranhas.

The wimple-piranhas eat scales of other fish. Their lower jaw is longer than the upper and their teeth are everted, which enables them to scrape the scales of their prey in a single upward swipe. In the presence of wary potential prey, they live on insects and other small invertebrates.

The genera of South American "salmons" have many features that suggest they are a primitive group. *Catabasis* is known only from a single preserved specimen. These fish are presumed to be extant but none have been seen since this fish was caught in 1900. *Salminus* is called a *dourados* by the Brazilians and is apparently the most primitive characiform known. Despite its importance as a genus of food and sport fish the classification of its four species is uncertain.

Acestrorhynchus is the Neotropical genus equivalent to the African genus *Hepsetus* but to exemplify the plethora of species and paucity of knowledge of South American characins, virtually nothing is known about it.

The family of freshwater hatchet fish is an exception to the above. It consists of deep-bodied fish, with long pectoral fins, that rarely exceed 4in (10cm) and are capable of powered flight. The deep chest houses powerful muscles which are necessary for turning the pectoral fins into wings. Prior to flight, hatchet fish may "taxi" for distances up to 40ft (12m), for most of which the tail and chest trail in the water. The flight phase is marked by a buzzing caused by the very rapid flapping of the fins. The flight distance rarely exceeds 5ft (1.5m) but they have been seen at a height of 3ft (90cm) above the water. The energy cost of flight to the fish is unknown, but it is thought that flight is used when frightened by predators. Normally hatchet fish are found near the water surface feeding on insects. Species of *Triportheus* also have their chest developed into a sort of keel and have large wing-like pectoral fins, similar to those of the hatchet fish. These fish are able to use the breast muscles and pectoral fins to jump about 3.3ft (1m) above the water's surface. This is to escape predators but cannot be considered real flight.

Most characins are generalized egg-scatterers but in some there is specialized breeding behavior.

The male glandulocaudines have scales modified into special glands, known as "caudal glands," at the base of the caudal fin. To attract a female these glands secrete a pheromone—a chemical the opposite sex are supposed to find irresistible. If the pheromone alone is insufficient to attract a mate, some males are also equipped with a worm-like lure to signal to the female of his choice. It is unknown whether this is intended to be a prey mimic or whether it is a visual cue to induce the female to approach.

In the family Lebiasinidae is the Splashing tetra. To avoid the high predation on eggs in water the Splashing tetra lays its eggs on overhanging leaves or rocks. The male courts a gravid female until the point of egg-laying is reached. Leading her to the overhang of his choice about 1in (3cm) above the water, he makes trial jumps up to this spawning site. The female then follows, adheres briefly to its surface, using water surface tension, and lays a few eggs. The male then leaps and fertilizes them. This process continues until about 200 eggs are laid and fertilized. After spawning the female goes on her way but the male remains nearby to splash water over the eggs until they hatch. The eggs take about three days to hatch and once the fry fall into the water the male's "nursemaid" activities are over.

One of the South American characins, *Brycon petrosus*, indulges in terrestrial group spawning. Males are distinguished by a convex anal fin and short, bony spicules on the fin rays. About 50 adults move by lateral undulations or tail flips onto the banks and lay eggs on the damp ground. There is no parental care and the eggs take about 2 days to hatch.

Tetras, fishes beloved of aquarists, have received their common name from a contraction of their scientific group name, Tetragonopterini. Many of these highly successful fishes are brilliantly colored which, apart from rendering them commercially important in the aquarist world, holds the members of shoals together in the wild. Tetras are omnivorous to the extent that they will eat anything they can fit into their mouths. Within this group is the Mexican blind cave characin, discussed on p92.

BB

There are about 2,400 species of **catfishes**, assigned to some 30 families. Most are tropical freshwater fishes, some inhabit temperate regions (Ictaluridae, Siluridae, Diplomystidae and Bagridae) and two families (Plotosidae and Ariidae) are marine.

Catfishes are so named because of their long barbels giving them a bewhiskered appearance (though barbels are not present in all species and are not a defining character of the group). Characters defining catfishes include the fusion of the first 4–8 vertebrae, often with modification of the chain of bones connecting the swim bladder to the inner ear (Weberian apparatus); lack of parietal bones; unique arrangement of blood vessels in the head; absence of typical body scales and strong dorsal and pectoral fin spines.

Although catfishes lack typical scales, the bodies of many are not entirely naked. Doradids, sisorids and amphiliids have bony scutes around the sensory pores of the lateral line and sometimes along the back. Loricariids and callichthyids may be completely encased in these scutes. Strong serrated pectoral and dorsal fin spines are widespread in catfishes. Locking mechanisms keep the spines erect and these coupled with the bony armor must deter potential predators. Catfish swim bladders may be partially or completely enclosed in a bony capsule. Why this should be is not clear, since the most obvious correlation, a reduction of the swim bladder with benthic habits, does not hold. For example, reduced and encapsulated swim bladders occur in active, fast-swimming species (of Hypophthalmidae and Ageniosidae) while the bottom-dwelling electric catfishes (Malapteruridae) have the largest swim bladders of any catfish.

There are more catfish species in South

▲ **A multitude laid bare.** Being nocturnal creatures and bottom-dwellers catfish are unfamiliar fish: they are, however, far more abundant than is generally realized. During the rainy season many move into flood plains to feed or breed. At the onset of the dry season those trapped in hollows will die unless, like some of the members of the family Clariidae, they can move over land back to the main river. This sad spectacle was seen in Lake Katavi, Tanzania.

▶ **Sublime symbolism.** The members of the family Ariidae are one of the two groups of catfish that have marine as well as freshwater representatives. In the Caribbean ariids are called crucifix fish because of the fancied likeness to Christ on the Cross presented by bones on the underside of the skull. The skull is often decorated and sold as a curio. Ariids lay a few large eggs which are protected in the mouth.

America than in the rest of their area of distribution. Both the world's smallest and largest catfishes occur here; *Scoloplax* (family Scoloplacidae) of Bolivia is a minute, partially armored fish whose total adult length is less than 0.5in (13mm) whereas *Paulicea* family (Pimelodidae) from Amazonia grows to more than 10ft (about 3m). Of the 16 families in South America most live in the Amazon Basin, but four are endemic to the Andes.

The largest of all catfish families is the Loricariidae with over 600 species. The mouth of these armored forms is sucker-like with thin, often comb-like teeth adapted to scraping algal mats. Most are active at night and hide during the day in crevices and logs. The males of some species bear long spines on their opercular apparatus (ie the bones forming the gill cover) and use them in cheek-to-cheek territoriality fights with other males. *Farlowella* species are long and thin and resemble dead twigs.

Closely related to the loricariids are the Astroblepidae (30 species) inhabiting Andean torrents. These are able to climb smooth, almost vertical rock faces by utilizing the muscles of the ventral surface and pelvic fins to induce suction.

The Callichthyidae have mail-like plates thought to resist desiccation when ponds dry up. Two genera (*Callichthys* and *Hoplosternum*) can withstand marked temperature changes and can move over dry land, using their pectoral spines for locomotion. They also build floating bubble nests. *Corydoras* is well-known to aquarists, who have recorded the breeding habits and development of many species.

The Doradidae vary greatly in size from *Physopyxis* (2in, 5cm) to *Megalodoras* (3.3ft, 1m). Most species are bottom dwellers and, surprisingly, play an important part in seed dispersal by their fruit-eating habits. The seeds are not digested and pass through the fish unharmed.

The Pimelodidae with 300 species is a family of great morphological diversity and includes some of the largest known catfishes. Most species are omnivorous, but the larger are fish-eaters or carnivores. One species has even been recorded as having eaten monkeys that fell in the river. Pimelodids form an important catfishery in parts of the Amazon Basin.

A strange family is the Trichomycteridae (280 species). Some are parasites, inhabiting and laying their eggs in the gill cavities of the larger pimelodid catfishes. The "candiru" is a notorious representative: mammals (including humans) have had their urethra penetrated by this slender fish while urinating in the water. The candiru probably mistakes the flow of urine for water being expelled from the gill chamber of a large catfish. As well as several eyeless species there are also two peculiar nonparasitic genera which have large fat-filled organs above the pectoral fins. One of these, *Sarcoglanis*, known only from a single specimen 1.5in (4cm) long, was collected in 1925 by Dr Carl Ternetz from the San Gabriel Rapids on the Rio Negro. Forty years later Dr George Myers, visiting the same locality, caught another similar fish but belonging to a new genus. Nothing is known about these puzzling forms.

The Cetopsidae (12 species) is also a poorly known group. Some species prey on other catfishes by biting out circular pieces of flesh with their saw-like teeth.

The Auchenipteridae (60 species) contains species that have conspicuous spots and stripes. They range from Panama to La Plata and are nocturnal, detrital feeders, inhabiting hollow logs by day where they line up in ranks.

The Hypophthalmidae are most unusual. Unlike most other catfishes they feed on plankton which they sieve from the water through fine gill rakers. Long barbels help to funnel the plankton into the mouth. As it is a surface feeder *Hypophthalmus* has high fat content and paper-thin bones to increase buoyancy.

Of the eight families of catfishes in Africa, only three are endemic. Four are shared with Asia and one, the Ariidae, also occurs in the coastal waters of Asia, Australia and North and South America. Although there is less diversity in form among African catfishes than there is among South American ones, there are many unusual forms, some displaying remarkable parallels with those of South America. The richest diversity of species in Africa occurs in the principal equatorial river basin, the Zaïre, which may be regarded as Africa's equivalent of the Amazon.

A major difference between the continents, however, is the series of rift valley great lakes in Africa; some of these harbor endemic groups of catfishes.

The most widespread family is the Bagridae (over 100 species). Some species of *Bagrus*, a Nilotic catfish genus, weigh over 11lb (5kg). Small bagrids, Zaïrean endemics, live in torrents, while a "flock" of several *Chrysichthys* species inhabits Lake Tanganyika. This generalized family also has members in Asia.

The Clariidae (about 30 species and 10

genera) are long-bodied with long dorsal and anal fins and broad flat heads. Some species have an organ at the top of the gill chamber that enables them to breathe atmospheric air and so survive when water is deoxygenated. Clariids, like the South American callichthyids, can travel overland from one water body to another. During a drought some rivers appear to be alive with the heaving, wriggling bodies of *Clarias*. The largest clariid is *Heterobranchus*, exceeding 110lb (50kg). Other genera are small, anguilliform fishes with burrowing habits; *Uegitglanis* from Somalia is subterranean and eyeless; *Clarias cavernicola* from Namibia is also eyeless. The family also occurs in Asia, but there are fewer species.

The endemic family Malapteruridae with its two species is the only family of electric catfishes. All catfishes appear capable of *detecting* electrical activity, but only *Malapterurus* is capable of producing it. The dense, fatty electric organ covers the flanks of the fish and gives it a cylindrical, sausage-shaped appearance. The strong electric impulses (up to 450 volts) are used for both defense and stunning prey. Some specimens exceed 3.3ft (1m) in length and weigh up to 44lb (20kg).

The family Mochokidae is exclusively African. Over 100 of its 150 species belong to the genus *Synodontis*. A few species of that genus swim upside down to utilize food on the surface as well as feeding normally on

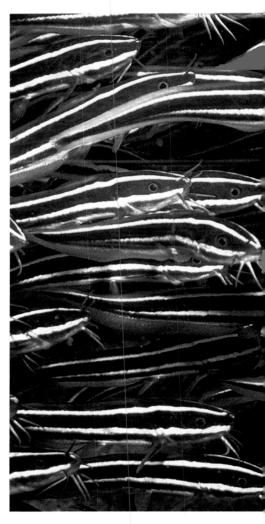

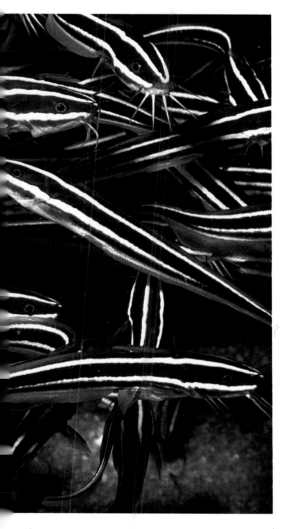

▲ **Shades of youth.** The family of eeltail catfishes (Plotosidae) has many marine representatives. The bright and conspicuous markings of *Plotosus lineatus* (sometimes called the Barber eel) are interpreted as a warning that this species has poisonous glands in its dorsal and pectoral fins. However, these bright colors are only present in the young. The adults are a dull brown.

◄ **Invisible camouflage.** Not all catfishes are bottom-dwellers. Some, for example those of the genus *Schilbe* in Africa, of *Pangasius* in Southeast Asia and of *Helogenes* in South America, are mid-water shoaling species. Among these at least two, *Physailia pellucida* and *Kryptopterus bicirrhus* (seen here) in Southeast Asia, have become transparent as a means of camouflage. The physiology of transparency is an enigma. It does not persist for long after death.

the bottom. This habit has led to the common name of the family being "upside-down catfishes."

The endemic family Amphiliidae contains about 45 small species. Some (eg *Phractura* and *Andersonia*) display remarkable parallelism with the South American *Farlowella* (Loricariidae) in their elongate, plated bodies. Amphiliids live largely in the faster, cooler upper reaches of rivers, clinging to the cobbled substrate.

The Schilbeidae, a family shared with Asia, has about 20 species in Africa. They have a short dorsal fin and compressed, rather deep bodies. They are fast-swimming shoalers which, in their large numbers, are both important predators on other fishes and in their turn form a large food source for fish-eating perches. Schilbeids are ubiquitous fishes that can change their diets easily (euryphagous) and have become quickly adapted to artificial situations such as dammed lakes and reservoirs.

After carps and their allies catfishes are the dominant element of Asia's fish fauna. Compared with African catfishes, Asian catfishes are not well known, scattered as they are throughout the Indonesian islands and isolated rivers and lakes of China and high Asia. Twelve families occur in and around the continent, seven of which are endemic.

The Bagridae are widely distributed with the species-rich genus *Mystus* being typical. *Bagrichthys* from Borneo and Sumatra is unusual in that the dorsal fin spine of the adult is nearly the length of the fish's body.

The Siluridae are a significant family with species in Eurasia, Japan, and offshore islands. The family contains the glass catfish, *Kryptopterus*, a favorite of aquarists, as well as the 6.5ft (2m) long voracious predator *Wallago*. This giant follows shoals of carps in their upstream migrations and can leap clear of the water during a feeding frenzy.

Species of the endemic families Sisoridae (100 species) and Amblycipitidae (30 species) are small inhabitants of mountain streams, clinging to the substrate by the partial vacuum caused by corrugations of their undersides. The two species of the small family Chacidae from Borneo are well-camouflaged, flattened fishes with cavernous mouths and large heads. They resemble some angler fishes.

The Pangasiidae family, containing about 10 species, is possibly the most economically important of the Southeast Asian catfishes. In Thailand *Pangasius* species have been pond-reared on fruit and vegetables for over a century. One of the world's largest fresh-water fishes, *Pangasianodon* occurs in the Mekong river, growing to 6.5ft (2m). Despite the evidence from travelers' tales, it too is vegetarian.

The family Plotosidae contains about 40 species, some of which live in the Indo-Pacific Ocean. Two genera, *Tandanus* and *Neosilurus* (the eel-tailed catfishes), live in the fresh waters of Australia and New Guinea. Specimens of *Tandanus* can weigh up to 15lb (7kg). The fishes build circular nests, about 6.5ft (2m) in diameter, from pebbles, gravel and sticks. The several thousand eggs are guarded by the male until they hatch after seven days. The young of *Plotosus* collect into moving "feeding-balls" which make them appear like sea urchins. Plotosids are notorious for the painful and dangerous wounds they inflict with their pectoral spines which have venomous glands at their base.

Of the Clariidae the widespread species *Clarias batrachus* has been introduced into Florida, USA, where it is known as the Walking catfish. Closely related to the Clariidae is the family Heteropneustidae, species of which possess long air sacs that extend backwards from each gill cavity.

The sea cats (the family Ariidae) have a circumtropical, largely marine distribution. Their most distinctive feature is that the males carry the eggs in their mouth. Up to 50 large, fertilized eggs will be carried for as long as two months, during which time the male starves.

Apart from a few ariid species reaching coastal regions, only one family, the Ictaluridae, is present in North America, with its 7 genera comprising some 50 species. The flatheads (*Pylodictis* species) are the largest, growing to some 88lb (40kg). The blue and channel catfishes (*Ictalurus* species) form the basis of a large catfishery in the Great Lakes and the Mississippi valley. The madtoms (*Noturus* species) are so named because they have venomous glands at the bases of their pectoral fins. There are three cave-dwelling (troglobitic), eyeless ictalurids which appear to have evolved independently. The genus *Prietella* is known only from a well in Coahuila, Mexico; *Satan* and *Trogloglanis* species have only appeared in 1,000ft (300m) deep artesian wells near San Antonio in Texas. It is thought they live in deep water-bearing strata.

Apart from introduced ictalurids only the family Siluridae is present in Europe. The European wels occurs in central and eastern Europe, growing to 16ft (5m) and over 660lb (300kg); adults of 15 years have been recorded.   GJH

The **cyprinoids** form a major lineage of largely freshwater, egg-laying fishes. All lack jaw teeth but most have a pair of enlarged bones in the pharynx, the teeth of which work against the partner bone and a pad on the base of the skull. A less conspicuous unifying feature is a small bone (the kinethmoid) which enables the upper jaw to be protruded. Cyprinoids are indigenous to Eurasia, Africa, and North America. Unlike the other major otophysan lineages they are not native to South America and Australia.

Of the six families, with over 2,500 species, by far the largest is the family Cyprinidae with over 2,000. The Cyprinidae—the chubs, minnows, mahseers, carps, barbs, ghillimentjes etc—reflect the distribution of the cyprinoids and are well known to both freshwater anglers and aquarists. Even in areas where they never lived naturally, many are familiar to fishermen and pond-keepers as well as to gourmets.

The carp epitomizes the family. Probably native to Central Europe and Asia, it has been introduced to all continents capable of supporting fish life. The carp is extremely tolerant of a wide range of conditions. In Central Africa, where it was introduced to provide food for expatriates, it has colonized areas so successfully that it is now the commonest cyprinid. In the United Kingdom, to which it was probably introduced in Roman times, it is loved by anglers, for whom catching a 40lb (18kg) specimen is a lifetime's goal. In South Africa, where the carp was introduced in the early part of this century, an 83lb (38kg) specimen was caught. The Japanese in particular have cultivated carps as objects of beauty: several hundred years of intensive breeding has released the potential colors and many carps (*koi*) are sold for high prices to beautify ponds and aquaria. In its native Eurasia it is bred commercially for food. Even there modifications have been made. Careful selection firstly produced carp with a few scales, then with none. Further selective breeding has resulted in strains lacking the hair-like intermuscular bones that create problems of decorum for diners.

The majority of cyprinids are smallish fishes, ie 4–6in (10–15cm) long when adult. But, as ever with fish, there are exceptions. The mahseer of the Himalayan and Indian rivers reach over 6ft (1.8m) long and can weigh 120lb (54kg). In North America the squawfish (*Ptychocheilus*) of the Colorado and Sacramento rivers, which were an important food source to the American

Indians of those areas (hence the common name), used to grow to over 6ft (1.8m) long. Now they are practically extinct in the Colorado (because of damming) and much smaller and rarer in the Sacramento (because of overfishing). Of similar length is the yellow-cheek from the Amur River in northern China. *Elopichthys* and *Ptychocheilus* are unusual among cyprinids (which are toothless) in that they are specialized fish-eaters. Other, but smaller, examples of fish-eaters are *Barbus mariae*, from a few rivers in East Africa; *Luciobrama macrocephalus* from southern China—a fish with a disproportionately elongate head; and *Macrochirichthys macrochirus* from the Mekong River. The last is a strongly compressed fish with a large, angled mouth and a hook and notch on the lower jaw. It is capable of raising its head to increase the gape when lunging at its prey.

Most cyprinids, including the mahseer, will eat almost anything: detritus, algae, mollusks, insects, arthropods, sausages, cheese sandwiches and luncheon meat. The bighead carps (*Hypophthalmichthys*) of China are specialized plankton feeders with gill rakers modified into an elaborate filtering organ. The grass-carp subsists on plant food and has been introduced to many countries to clear weeds from canals, rivers and lakes.

The shape and distribution of the pharyngeal teeth often indicate the diet. Mollusk-eaters have crushing molar-like teeth, closely packed; fish-eaters have thin, hooked teeth; vegetarians have thin, knife-like teeth for shredding. Omnivores come somewhere in the middle. But even within one species the teeth can vary. In Africa fish of the species *Barbus altianalis* living in a lake with no snails have "middle-of-the-road" type teeth, while those in a lake a few miles away rich in snails have thicker, lower, more rounded teeth. The young all start off with the same type of teeth which

▲ **The carp** TOP (foreground) has been cultivated for centuries in Europe. Various forms, showing degrees of reduction in scales, are now known. The Crucian carp (*Carassius carassius*) from Asia is a much smaller species and a close relative of the goldfish.

▲**Push fish**—a pair of Apollo sharks (*Luciosoma setigerum*) engaged in an open-mouth, sideways-pushing display. This species is distributed in Southeast Asia.

◄**Most loaches** are eel-like in shape but many members of the southern Asian genus *Botia* are strongly laterally compressed. Seen here is *Botia hymenophysa* from Sumatra, Indonesia.

makes cyprinid classification very difficult.

The widespread and species-rich genus *Barbus* derives its name from the (usually) four barbels around the mouth which are provided with taste buds so that the fish can taste the substrate before eating. A particular specialization of some African species is to vary the shape and thickness of the mouth and lips according to diet. A broad-mouthed form with a wide, sharp-edged lower jaw will feed on epilithic algae. A narrow-mouthed form with thick "rubber" lips feeds by sucking up stones and their associated fauna. That these two extremes are found in the same species explains why what is now regarded as one species (*B. intermedius*) formerly had over 50 scientific names.

Most cyprinids do not exhibit sexual dimorphism but some of the small *Barbus* species do. In Central Zaïre, living among submerged tree roots, are small "butterfly barbs," 1.5in (4cm) long, including *Barbus hulstaerti* and *B. papilio*. In these strikingly marked species the males and females have conspicuously different color patterns.

Although generally the cyprinids are not as brilliantly colored as the characins, some of the Southeast Asian *Rasbora* species have come close. The small Malaysian species *Rasbora brittani* and *R. axelrodi* are the cyprinid equivalents of the popular glow-light and neon tetras (order Characiformes).

Totally without color, however, are the subterranean cyprinids. Members of the genera *Barbus*, *Garra* and *Caecocypris* have lost all pigment—and their eyes—as a result of living in caves. They are discussed in detail in "Fish Underground" (pp92–93). The epigean *Garra* species are found in Africa, India and Southeast Asia. They are bottom-dwelling fishes with a suctorial and sensory disk on the underside of the head. The related genus *Labeo*, with a similar distribution, has an elaborate suctorial mouth and grazes on algae. One African species often feeds on the flanks of submerged hippopotamuses.

In the cold, mountain streams of India and Tibet live the poorly known snow-trouts (Schizothoracines), cyprinids that imitate the life-style of trout and salmon. They are elongate fish, up to 1ft (30cm) long with very small scales (or none at all) except for a row of tile-like scales along the base of the anal fin. Nepalese fishermen capture snow-trouts by fashioning a worm-shaped wire surrounded by a loop which is tightened when the fish strikes at the "worm."

Although earlier it was stressed that cyprinids are essentially freshwater fishes some can tolerate considerable degrees of salinity. In Japan species of *Tribolodon* have been found up to 3mi (5km) out at sea. In Europe the familiar freshwater roach and bream live in the Baltic Sea at about 50 percent salinity. These are, however, among the few exceptions.

As if cyprinids are not already full of eccentric habits, at least two species are known to get drunk! In Southeast Asia both *Leptobarbus* and *Hampala* gorge themselves on the fermented fruit of the chaulmoogra tree when it drops into the water. They even congregate before "opening time." When intoxicated they float helpless in the water, but are relatively safe as their flesh is now unpalatable. Perhaps as a compensation for such antisocial cyprinid behavior the Eurasian tench has gained a reputation from countrymen (whose observation is often acute) of being a doctor fish. It is reported that injured fish seek out tench and rub their wounds in its slime. It is true that the tench has a copious coating of slime, but as for its healing properties . . . ?

The suckers (Catostomidae) have many species in North America and a handful in north Asia. For a long time they were thought to be the most primitive cyprinoids. This was because of the shape of their pharyngeal bones and teeth. The pharyngeal bone is formed from one of the plain, cylindrical bones in the fifth gill arch. In catostomids, however, it is less modified and its homology is more evident. Suckers have also developed highly complex sacs from the upper gill-arch bones and it now seems likely, taking into account their distribution, that they are a highly specialized group of cyprinoids. They are innocuous, unspectacular fish, apart from two genera, one in China (*Myxocyprinus*) and one in the Colorado River (*Xyrauchen*). Both are deep-bodied, with a triangular profile. The function of this peculiar shape (the others are just "fish"-shaped) is to force them close to the bottom of the river during flash floods. Both live in rivers susceptible to flash floods. These suckers are therefore a good example of parallel evolution.

The loaches are a family of eel-like fishes with minute, embedded scales and a plethora of barbels around the mouth. Bony processes enclose most, or all, of the swim bladder, making its normal volume changes rather awkward. All the cyprinoids have a tube connecting the swim bladder to the pharynx, allowing the fish to swallow or expel air. But with the constricted swim bladder loaches use this more often than many. One species, known as the Weather fish, from eastern Europe has been kept for centuries by peasants as a living barometer. Its agitation in expressing air as the atmospheric pressure increases with, say, the approach of thunderstorms made it one of the earliest weather-forecasters.

Most loaches have small dorsal and anal fins symmetrically placed near the rear of the body. The poorly known *Vaillantella* has a dorsal fin the length of the body. Loaches can be divided into two subgroups: those that have an erectile spine below the eye and those that do not. Many are secretive fish, liking to hide under stones during the day. It was an overdue discovery when the first cave-living species was found in Iran in 1976. Since then two more have been found in southwest China.

Loaches live in Eurasia, not in Africa (apart from an arguably introduced species in European North Africa), except for the enigmatic *Noemacheilus abyssinicus*. A Mr Degen was collecting for the British Museum in Ethiopia in 1900. His collection from the mouth of a feeder stream entering Lake Tsana purportedly contained the specimen described under that name some years later. No more have ever been found, but again, no one has revisited the site and used his collecting techniques. Or perhaps one jar could have been misplaced on a museum shelf.

Gyrinocheilids, mistakenly known in the aquarium trade as Siamese algal eaters, sift detritus. There are only three or four species, all from Southeast Asia. They have a ventral, protrusile mouth, like the hose of a vacuum cleaner. With this they suck in the fine substrate and filter out the edible material. *Gyrinocheilus* lacks a pharyngeal tooth apparatus; whether this is lost or has never been developed is unknown. The gyrinocheilids are unique among cyprinoids in that the gill cover is sealed to the body for most of its length leaving top and bottom openings. The top opening is covered by a valve and takes *in* water to oxygenate the gills and expels it through the bottom opening. Thus breathing is through the gill cover rather than the mouth.

Almost nothing is known of the Indo-Chinese psilorhynchids. They are small, camouflaged bottom-living fishes.

▼▶ **Representative members** of the orders of milk fishes, characins, catfishes and cyprinoids. (1) *Gobiobotia longibarba*, a poorly known species of gudgeon or loach-like cyprinoid from China (6in, 15cm). (2) Two examples of *Gastromyzon*, a hillstream cyprinoid adapted for life in the torrential waters of South and Southeast Asia by having paired fins forming sucking disks (3in, 8cm). (3) *Xyrauchen texanus*, a rare species of cyprinoid from the Colorado River, USA (24in, 60cm). (4) A milk fish (*Chanos chanos*), from shallow waters of the Indian Ocean and adjacent fresh waters (6.5ft, 2m). (5) *Luciobrama*, a pike-like cyprinoid predator which however lacks teeth on the jaws (3.3ft, 1m). (6) *Rhaphiodon*, a highly specialized characoid piscivore from South America (16in, 40cm). (7) A tiger fish (genus *Hydrocynus*), an African characoid occurring in both rivers and lakes (maximum length about 6.5ft, 2m). (8) A species of sea cat, from the catfish family Ariidae. (9) Two examples of *Vandellia cirrhosa*, a species of candiru (2.5in, 6cm), investigating the gills of a catfish.

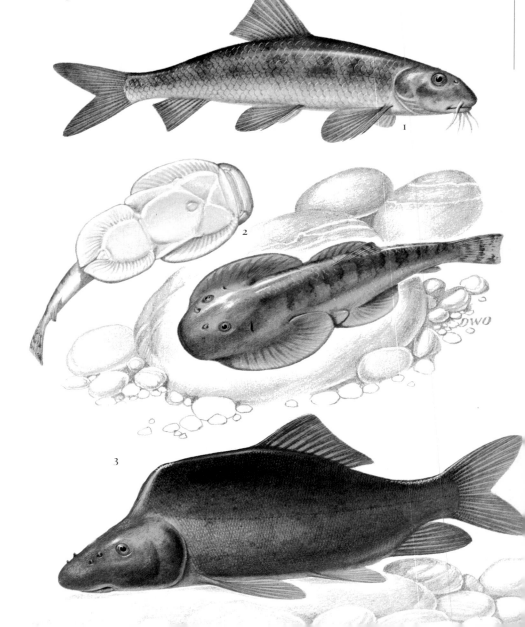

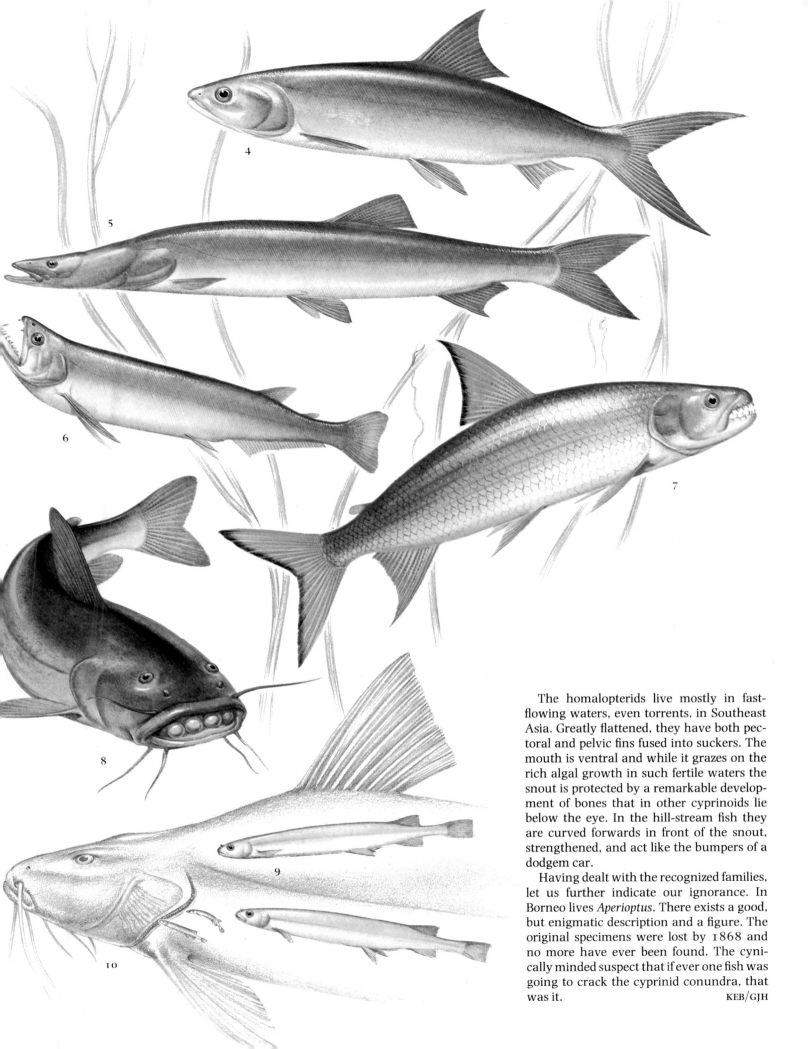

The homalopterids live mostly in fast-flowing waters, even torrents, in Southeast Asia. Greatly flattened, they have both pectoral and pelvic fins fused into suckers. The mouth is ventral and while it grazes on the rich algal growth in such fertile waters the snout is protected by a remarkable development of bones that in other cyprinoids lie below the eye. In the hill-stream fish they are curved forwards in front of the snout, strengthened, and act like the bumpers of a dodgem car.

Having dealt with the recognized families, let us further indicate our ignorance. In Borneo lives *Aperioptus*. There exists a good, but enigmatic description and a figure. The original specimens were lost by 1868 and no more have ever been found. The cynically minded suspect that if ever one fish was going to crack the cyprinid conundra, that was it.   KEB/GJH

Fish underground

The locations, forms and lives of cave fishes

Chologaster cornutus

There are now known to be about 38 species of fishes, belonging to 13 different families, that spend their lives in lightless, underground waters. In some cases it is uncertain whether an underground population represents a separate species or merely a highly modified population of a surface-living (epigean) species.

Cave fishes are colorless and have either minute eyes or no eyes. The scales are reduced by varying degrees in different species. Some fishes living under rocks in rapids may also have the same characteristics. Not all "cave fishes" live in caves. Some, for example, live in water-bearing strata (aquifers) where the rock is honeycombed with water-filled channels.

Subterranean fishes occur in tropical and warm temperate countries that have not been affected by recent glaciation. In Australia two species, an eleotrid and a synbranchid, live in the Yardee Creek wells on the North West Cape. Madagascar has two eleotrids. Africa has a barb in Zaïre, a synbranchid in Mauritania and a clariid catfish in Namibia; three species, a catfish and two cyprinids, live in Somalia. Oman has two species of the cyprinid genus *Garra*—neither yet described scientifically. Iran has a subterranean loach and another garrine cyprinid; Iraq, yet another garrine (*Typhlogarra widdowsoni*) and *Caecocypris*, a cyprinid of unknown affinities. Wells in Kerala, southern India, hold *Horaglanis*, a small catfish that subsequent investigation has suggested does not belong to the family in which it was originally placed (Clariidae). Three species (two loaches and yet another garrine) have recently been found in China. Cuba has two ophidioids, Mexico has one and also has characoids and a synbranchid. The subterranean fauna of Brazil consists of catfishes and characoids. The USA has a rich cave fauna in many sites from the Ozark and Cumberland plateaux to Texas comprising catfish and ambylopsids. There may also be cave fish in New Guinea and Thailand. Europe has no cave fish but there is a cave-adapted amphibian (*Proteus*) in Yugoslavia.

The eleotrids of Madagascar and Australia are related to the gobies and are fundamentally marine fishes, as are the ophidioids of Cuba and Mexico. Fishes of the family Ophidiidae show how difficult it is to categorize cave fishes neatly. They are mostly fishes living in deepish water of somewhat reclusive habit. Shallow-water representatives are likely to be found in salt-water-bearing strata vertically inshore in islands. When, as in the Bahamas, an artesian well is sunk, their appearance should not be unexpected. In the geological past fishes living in such conditions could have been trapped in such underground waters as land masses moved and then slowly adapted themselves to brackish or fresh water over a long period of time. Such speculations have been proposed to explain the presence of *Stygichthys* and *Lucifuga* in Cuba. How other cave fish came to live where they do is uncertain. There is some evidence from *Chologaster*, a close relative of the American ambylopsids, of preadaptation. *Chologaster* has small eyes and actively shuns light. In desert areas the fish may well have, where possible, followed the falling water-table underground.

So far as we know cave fish live longer than their surface-living relatives. This may be a response to their irregular and sparse food supply, which comes into the cave during floods as detritus or is provided by other cave animals all of which are ultimately supported by "the outside."

Reproduction in cave fishes has never been observed in the wild, except in the Cuban ophidioids, which give birth to fully formed young. Other cave-fish groups are probably egg-layers. In captivity the only form bred (and commercially available to aquarists) is the so-called *Anoptichthys jordani* which recent research has shown to be subterranean populations of the widespread *Astyanax fasciatus*. The reproductive strategies of its surface-living and subterranean populations are similar.

It is important to be able to breed cave fishes because, first, wild populations are low and, second, we cannot answer questions about them until we have done so. At least two species in captivity have been reared until sexually ripe, but all the individuals died before spawning. It seems that a trigger to induce spawning is missing. A possible clue to a trigger comes from caves in Zaïre. Here the young are found after the rains—the force of the rain water flooding into the caves is enough to flatten a gasoline can to the contours of the rock against which it lodges. It is not known what effect changes of temperature or other factors may have, but experiments are now being made using current-machines.   KEB

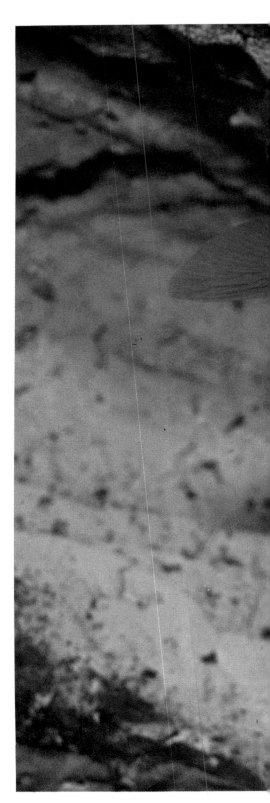

◄► **The relinquishing of sight.** These North
American species are superficially alike.
Chologaster shuns light and hides under stones.
A continuation of this proclivity could have led
to the occupation of dark caves and the
nondevelopment of eyes and pigment.

▼ **The only cave fish bred in captivity,**
"*Anoptichthys jordani,*" is actually a blind form
of the widespread species *Astyanax fasciatus.*

Amblyopsis spelaea

CODS, ANGLER FISHES...

Superorder Paracanthopterygii
About one thousand one hundred species in about 200 genera, about 30 families and 6 orders.

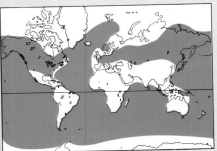

Position uncertain
(*Incertae sedis*)

Indostomidae
Beard fishes

Beard fishes Polymixiidae

Trout-perches
and allies

Amblyopsidae

Pirate perch
Aphredoderidae

Trout-perches
Percopsidae

Cods, hakes,
grenadiers . . .

Carapids or **pearl
fishes** Carapidae

Bregmacerotidae

Cods Gadidae

Eelpouts or
viviparous blennies
Zoarcidae

Grenadiers or
rat-tails Macrouridae

Hakes Merlucciidae

Moridae

Frog fishes and
angler fishes

Caulophrynidae

Ceratiidae

Linophrynidae

Oneirodidae

▲ **Outlines of representative species** of cods and angler fishes.

► **The Poor cod** is a common inshore fish of the Northeast Atlantic Ocean and Mediterranean. It is of little commercial importance but large numbers are caught by anglers.

OR many years the number of cod caught per year in the North Atlantic region was about 400 million. This is some indication of the familiarity achieved by fish from this superorder, though more often on the plate than in the aquarium. The superorder holds a bewildering variety of forms, from plain fishes like whiting and haddock to fishes with peculiar shapes and colors, fishes flattened from top to bottom, camouflaged fishes, fishes with lures and the bizarre parasitic angler fishes (see p104).

The superorder, containing six orders, was erected in 1966 to remove from the major grouping of spiny-finned fishes (Acanthopterygii) all the forms that were of a similar evolutionary grade but lacked the characteristics of the spiny-finned fishes. Although this act enabled the acanthopterygians to be somewhat more succinctly defined, the coherence of the new superorder of cods and angler fishes was still rather tenuous. Since that time there have been additions and rearrangements and some workers still have doubts about whether the paracanthopterygians constitute a natural group.

Most members of this superorder are marine, inhabiting both deep and shallow waters worldwide. Exceptional are individual species of some otherwise marine families which live in fresh waters and the handful of species in the order of trout-perches which are confined to the fresh waters of northern America.

The family of **beard fishes** with probably just one genus and a few species is believed to be the most primitive member of the superorder. Prior to its inclusion here it was thought to be one of the most primitive members of the Acanthopterygii.

Polymixia nobilis, the type species of the genus, lives at depths between 500 and 1,200ft (150–365m) in the North Pacific, Atlantic and Indian Oceans. It has a deep, compressed body, a large eye and a single dorsal fin about half the length of the body. There are two long, fleshy barbels under the chin. The jaws and palate have fine teeth. The body color varies from greenish to reddish-brown and the dorsal and caudal fins have black tips. Almost nothing is known of its biology. It grows to about 1ft (30cm) long and has no commercial value. *Polymixia japonica* is very similar—indeed some workers think it should not be classified as a separate species.

The **trout-perches** and their allies are small freshwater fishes from northern America. Fossils clearly belonging to this group are known from the Lower Cretaceous era (100–65 million years ago).

The trout-perches derive their common name from their vaguely "perch-like" first dorsal fin, which has spines at the front, and the presence of a "trout-like" adipose fin. There are only two species. *Percopsis transmontanus* comes from slow-flowing, weedy parts of the Columbian river system. It has scales with a comb-like free margin (ctenoid scales) and a cryptic greenish color with dark spots. Growing to about 4in (10cm) long it reaches only half the size of its widespread congener *Percopsis omiscomaycus* which occurs from the west coast of Canada to the Great lakes and the Mississippi-Missouri river system. Although two rows of spots are present, the body is translucent and the lining of the abdominal cavity can be seen through the sides. Both species feed on bottom-living invertebrates and are themselves eaten by predatory fishes.

The Pirate perch, from still and slow-flowing waters of the eastern USA, is the only member of the family Aphredoderidae. A sluggish, dark-hued fish, it grows to about 6in (15cm) long and lacks the adipose fin of the trout-perches. It is a predator on invertebrates and small fish. Its most unusual feature is its mobile vent. On

---

An Anomalous Fish

An interesting example of the difficulties involved in classifying fish is the case of *Indostomus paradoxus*. It is a peculiar little fish, scarcely 1in (2.5cm) long and native to Lake Indawgyi in Upper Burma. It is very slender, covered with bony plates, yet so prehensile or flexible that it can touch its nose with its tail. It has the unusual attribute for a fish of being able to move its head up and down. When frightened it tends to leap out of the water.

Because it has scutes and five isolated spines in front of the dorsal fin it was originally placed with the sticklebacks and pipefishes. Later research showed that not only was it quite unrelated to either group but that it did not also appear to be closely related to anything else either. It has a series of unique anatomical features that do not help to establish its relationships. These include a lower jaw 20 times longer than the upper, and hardly any muscles in the rear half of its body; the tail fin is worked by a series of long tendons.

Out of desperation, and on the basis of a few very tenuous features, it was placed in an order of its own in the Paracanthopterygii. Later workers have disagreed with this association, but have not been able to find a satisfactory home for it. So here it still sits, *incertae sedis*, "position uncertain."

The 6 Orders of Cods and Angler fishes

Position uncertain (*incertae sedis*)
Indostomus paradoxus
Distribution: Lake Indawgyi in Upper Burma.
Size: maximum length 1in (2.5cm).

Division (a): Polymixiomorpha

Beard fishes
Order: Polymixiiformes
Probably five species of the genus *Polymixia* and the family Polymixiidae.
Distribution: N Pacific, Atlantic and Indian oceans.
Size: maximum length 16in (40cm).

Division (b): Salmopercomorpha

Trout-perches and their allies
Order: Percopsiformes
Seven species in 7 genera and 3 families.
Distribution: N America.
Habitat: fresh water.
Size: length 6in (15cm).
Families and species include: Amblyopsidae, including **Southern cavefish** (*Typhlichthys subterraneus*); **Pirate perch** (Aphredoderidae, sole species *Aphredoderus sayanus*); **trout-perches** (family Percopsidae).

Cling fishes
Order: Gobiesociformes
About thirty-five genera of the family Gobiesocidae (number of species unknown).
Distribution: Atlantic, Indian and Pacific oceans in shallow waters; some species in fresh water in surrounding areas.
Size: most species under 4in (10cm); two reach over 12in (30cm).

Cods, hakes, grenadiers and their allies
Order: Gadiformes
Between three hundred and fifty and six hundred species in 70–100 genera and 9 families.
Distribution: northern hemisphere in cool marine coastal and moderately deep waters and cool fresh water.
Size: 1.5in–6.5ft (4cm–2m).
Families, genera and species include: **brotulids and cusk eels** (family Ophidiidae), including **kingklip** (*Genypterus capensis*); **carapids** or **pearl fishes** (family Carapidae); **eelpouts** or **viviparous blennies** (family Zoarcidae); Gadidae, including **Atlantic cod** (*Gadus morhua*), **bib** (*Trisopterus luscus*), **burbot** (*Lota lota*), **haddock** (*Melanogrammus aeglefinus*), **lings** (genus *Molva*), **North Pacific cod** (*Gadus macrocephalus*), **pollack** (*Pollachius pollachius*), **Poor cod** (*Trisopterus minutus*), **poutassou** (*Micromesistius poutassou*), **saithe** (*Pollachius virens*), **Wall eye pollack** or **whiting** (*Theragra chalcogrammus*), **whiting** (*Merlangius merlangus*); **hakes** (family Merlucciidae), including **North Atlantic hake** (*Merluccius merluccius*), **Pacific hake** (*M. productus*), **Stock fish** (*M. capensis*); Moridae, including **Red cod** (*Physiculus bachus*); **rat-tails** or **grenadiers** (family Macrouridae).

Frog fishes and angler fishes
Order: Lophiiformes
About two hundred and seventy species in about 60 genera and 15 or 16 families.
Distribution: oceans worldwide, mostly in deep water.
Size: maximum length 6.5ft (2m) but most are much smaller.
Species and families include: **bat fishes** (family Ogcocephalidae); **ceratiid angler fishes** (family Ceratiidae); **frog fishes** or **antenariids** (family Antenariidae), including **Sargassum fish** (*Histrio histrio*); **linophrynids** (family Linophrynidae); **lophiid angler** or **goose fishes** (family Lophiidae); **oneirodids** (family Oneirodidae).

Toad fishes
Order: Batrachoidiformes
Over sixty species in 19 genera of the family Batrachoididae.
Distribution: almost worldwide with species in coastal and deep sea waters and fresh water.
Size: maximum length 24in (60cm).
Genera include: **midshipmen** (genus *Porichthys*).

hatching, the anus is in a normal position, ie just in front of the anal fin. As the fish grows the anus moves forward until adulthood when it lies under the throat (see p97).

The family Amblyopsidae contains four genera, three of which live only in caves in the limestone regions of Kentucky and adjacent states. *Chologaster cornutus* is an eyed and pigmented fish found in sluggish and still waters from West Virginia to Georgia. Despite having functional eyes it shuns light and hides away under stones and logs during the day. *Chologaster agassizii* lives in subterranean waters in Kentucky and Tennessee. It lacks the dark stripe of its only congener but still has functional eyes. In both species, but especially the latter, there are series of raised sense organs on the skin.

The Southern cavefish lacks visible eyes, pigment and pelvic fins. Rows of papillae, sensitive to vibrations, are present on the body and on the tail fin. It is thought to have achieved its wide distribution, from Oklahoma to Tennessee and northern Alabama, by traveling through underground waterways. *Ambylopsis spelaea* is white, has minute eyes covered by skin, and tiny pelvic fins. Like its relatives it has vertical rows of sensory papillae on the body. Its reproductive strategy is unusual. The female lays a few relatively large eggs which, once fertilized, are carried in the gill chamber of the mother for up to ten weeks until they hatch.

The remaining genus, *Speoplatyrhinus*, is exceedingly rare and discussed in "Endangered Fishes" (see p17).

The order of **cods, hakes, grenadiers and their relatives** contains some of the commercially most important fishes, such as lings and whiting, as well as many smaller and deep-water species of biological but not financial importance.

They are mostly elongate fishes, having ventral fins well forward, often further forward than the pectoral fins. The fins lack spiny rays. The dorsal fin is very long and may be divided up into two or three separate units and may or may not be contiguous with the caudal fin, which in turn may or may not be contiguous with the long anal fin, which may be divided into two.

Almost all are marine fishes found in the cool waters of both hemispheres or in the deep sea. In some northern regions cooler currents enable them to live farther south than would be expected. The Pacific hake and the Pacific tomcod, for example, occur along the Pacific coast of America from Alaska to California.

Many of the commercially important species form shoals and the number of individuals they contained was, until severe overfishing had an effect, enormous. It was estimated that for many years 400 million cod were caught each year in the North Atlantic region. Bearing in mind the doubt about whether the North Pacific cod is the same species as the Atlantic cod, at any one time the number of individuals of that species was most impressive. As a female cod may produce over 6 million eggs it should not be too long before the fish stocks can regain their former abundance.

Some of the families in this order are of little importance and only brief reference will be made to them.

The Moridae is a worldwide family of deep-sea cods, found in all oceans almost from pole to pole. There are some 70 species often grouped into 17 genera. The configuration of dorsal and anal fins is variable but many species have a forked tail. Species in this family rarely exceed 3ft (90cm) in length. The biology of many species is unknown.

Antimora rostrata has been found in the North Pacific, North and South Atlantic and Indian Oceans at depths from 1,650 to 3,900ft (500–1,200m). The first ray of the first short-based dorsal fin is very long. The body color is dark violet to blackish brown. The Red cod—named from its death color—is common off New Zealand where it is used as a food fish. It occurs in much shallower waters than many of its relatives,

▲ ► ▼ **Some important species** belonging to the superorder Paracanthopterygii. (1) A North Atlantic hake (*Merluccius merluccius*; family Merlucciidae; order Gadiformes) (3.3ft, 1m). (2) A haddock (*Melanogrammus aeglefinus*; family Gadidae; order Gadiformes) (20in, 50cm). (3) The ventral view of a cling fish (*Chorisochismus dentex*; family Gobiesocidae; order Gobiesociformes) (4.7in, 12cm). (4) A trout-perch (*Percopsis omiscomaycus*; family Percopsidae; order Percopsiformes) (8in, 20cm).

4

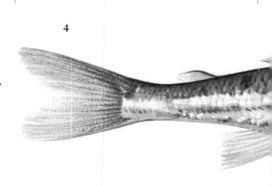

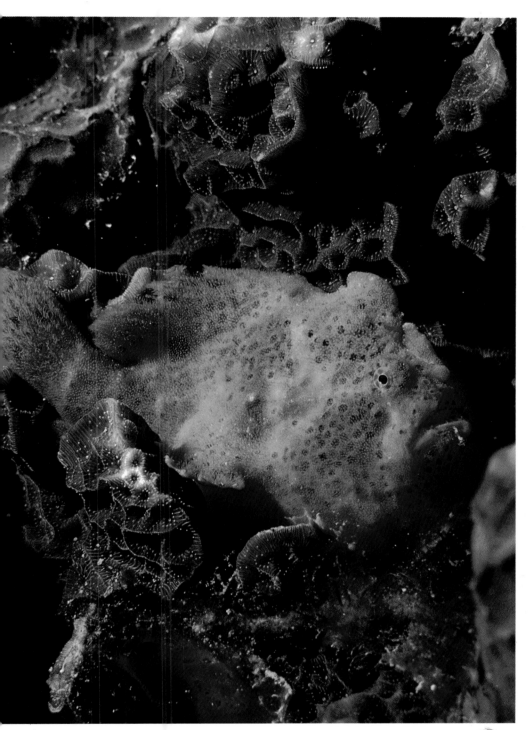

lie under the throat and they, and the muscular pectoral fins, are used for "walking" across the sea floor. The gill openings are near the hind end of the body, just before the pectoral fins. The eyes are placed dorsally and the mouth is below the snout.

Most species are inhabitants of deep water and all spend the day on the bottom waiting to eat prey tempted by their lures. Some kept in aquaria and some shallow-water species come to the surface at night, which suggests they might not be the inefficient swimmers they appear to be. The southern African species *Halieutea fitzsimonsi* has been recorded as entering brackish water. The Pacific deep-water species *Dibranchus stellulatus*, which grows to only an inch or so long, has an elaborate network of bony stars rather than nodules in the skin.

In the Far East bat fishes are called rattle fish. The inside of the fish is cleaned out and the skin left to dry in the wind. Some pebbles are placed inside it, the hole sewn up, the spines smoothed and the whole then used as a baby's rattle.

The family Chaunacidae is represented by one genus, probably by only one species, and is worldwide in distribution. Living at depths of 600–1,000ft (180–300m) it has a rough, pinkish skin, is compressed rather than depressed and has a large mouth. Its belly is highly inflatable.

The lophiid angler (or goose) fishes are large, depressed, bottom-living fishes. Their heads and mouths are enormous. *Lophius piscatorius* is found in both the North and South Atlantic, at depths down to 1,800ft (550m) outside the breeding season. It can reach 6ft (1.8m) in length and is a voracious predator. Normally an angler fish feeds on the bottom. Its outline is broken up by a series of irregular fleshy flaps and the prey is attracted by the lure. It is known that anglers occasionally come to the surface because one was found dead having choked

▲ **Lazing on the bottom,** an Atlantic species of frog fish (*Antennarius multiocellata*). The colors of frog fishes vary considerably.

▶ **Two species of batfishes** (frog fishes). (1) *Halieutichthys aculeatus* (4in, 10cm), (2) *Ogcocephalus parvus* (6in, 15cm).

▷ **Frog fish "skinscape"** OVERLEAF. The goosefish or Lophiid angler (*Lophius piscatorius*) is a shallow-water species with a flattened body and a large wide head. Its fishing lure is visible here in front of the eyes.

on a sea gull. Their voracity is further evidenced by many comments that *Lophius* usually comes up in a trawl with a full belly, having been unable to resist gorging itself on its fellow captives. *Lophius* is relatively uncritical about its diet and consumes any food item that comes close. As far as is known its only predator is the sperm whale in Icelandic waters.

In the North Atlantic angler fish move into deep water 6,000ft (1,800m) to spawn in spring. The egg mass forms a remarkable ribbon-like gelatinous structure up to 30ft (9m) long and 2ft (60cm) wide. The eggs usually form a single layer within this mass. The young hatch near the surface and feed on plankton, until they are 2–3in (5–8cm) long when they settle on the bottom.

The systematics of this group are not well known. Other genera, *Lophiodes*, *Lophiomus* and *Sladenia*, have been described from the Indo-Pacific region, but there is much dispute about the validity of some species included in them.

Although usually described as "flabby and revolting," the appearance of angler fish belies the nature of their flesh which is well textured and delicately flavored, popular in Europe where it is sold as monk fish. It has even been known for unscrupulous fishmongers to substitute scoops of angler fish tail for scampi. When breaded and fried it is very difficult to tell the difference.

The most bizarre members of this super-order, and probably the most bizarre vertebrates, are the ceratioid angler fishes. It was noted above that in the frog fishes and *Lophius* the first dorsal fin ray was displaced forwards towards the top of the head, where it developed a fleshy flap and by muscular control is moved around like a fishing rod with the fleshy flap forming the bait. While this system works well in shallow, sunlit seas, it is useless in the lightless waters where the ceratioids dwell. But they have retained the system and improved it. The fleshy flap has been developed into a some-times elaborate luminous organ called the esca, while the fishing pole has become very much longer, much more mobile, and is known as the illicium. Naturally, there are exceptions. The female *Neoceratias* lacks an illicium; in *Caulophryne* the esca is not luminous; *Gigantactis* has an illicium several times its body length whilst in *Melanocoetus* it is very short.

Many species also have a chin barbel, with several branches, the tips of which may be luminous. One species (*Himantolophus*),

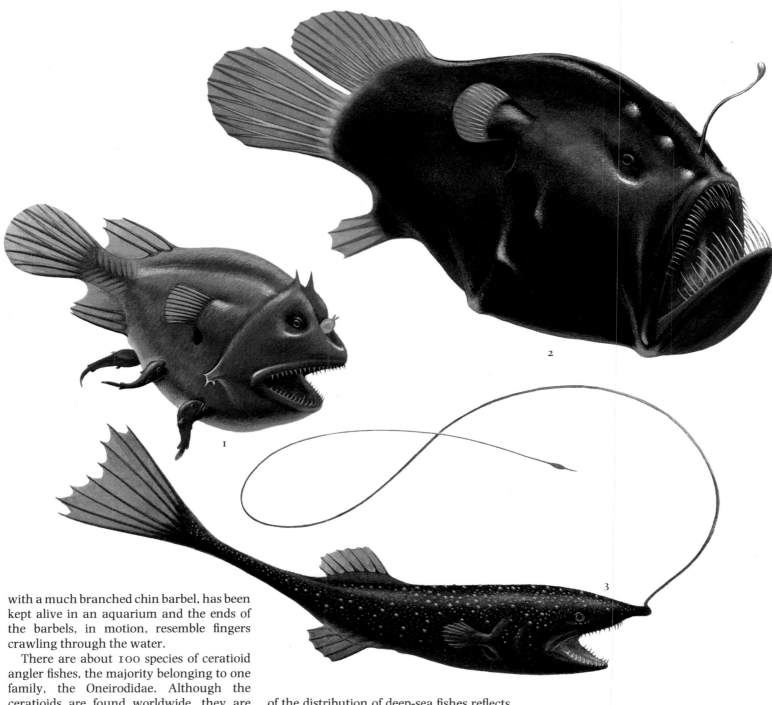

with a much branched chin barbel, has been kept alive in an aquarium and the ends of the barbels, in motion, resemble fingers crawling through the water.

There are about 100 species of ceratioid angler fishes, the majority belonging to one family, the Oneirodidae. Although the ceratioids are found worldwide, they are patchily distributed, preferring highly productive waters. Generally they are found at greater depths in the tropics than at the poles, but all these generalizations can be affected by local factors. Ceratioids like cool waters with a particular salinity, so hotter water extending from the surface to a considerable depth will form a barrier. In the tropics they have been found below 9,000ft (2,750m), whereas off Greenland one of the largest species, *Ceratias holboelli*, occasionally comes in to very shallow waters. Some species appear to have rather restricted distributions, but *Oneirodes eschrichti* occurs all over the world in suitable waters. However, it must be emphasized that our knowledge of the distribution of deep-sea fishes reflects little more than the distribution of the hauls of research vessels.

Angler fishes lack pelvic fins, but in some cases the pelvic fin bones are still present beneath the skin. In the other fins the number of rays is low, but the rays are thickened. The fan-shaped pectoral fin is, in some species, supported on a fleshy pedicel. The anal and dorsal fins are placed opposite one another.

In most species the skin is naked, but in *Himantolophus* and *Ceratias* bony nodules are present, and in the oneirodid *Spiniphryne* there are numerous close-set spines in the skin and along the bases of the fins.

In all species the skeleton is poorly

developed, both in terms of bone dimension and degree of calcification. Much cartilage persists and many bones are reduced to load-bearing struts. The operculum—a fan-shaped bone in most fishes—is reduced to a V in the oneirodids. To bear the large teeth the jaw bones are well developed by ceratioid standards, but fragile when compared with most other fishes. The lightening of the skeleton helps to achieve neutral buoyancy in the absence of a swim bladder.

Most ceratioids are dark brown or black but a few are gray and at least one is pallid. As far as we know most ceratioids are small fishes, rarely growing more than 6in (15cm) long. *Ceratias holboelli* is a comparative giant, reaching 3ft (90cm) in length. Ceratioids may be larger than we think, because deep-sea trawling is a cumbersome and inefficient process. To trawl at 1 mile (1.6km) deep may mean the boat is towing 3 miles (4.8km) of cable so the net is only moving very slowly and creating a great disturbance in the water. Larger and more agile individuals (if there are any) may well be able to avoid capture. Some of the globular species have their lateral-line organs set out from the body on stalks, to increase the fishes' awareness of pressure changes, and they may well be able to detect the approaching net without difficulty.

It is presumed that the lateral line of adult ceratioids is sensitive because their eyesight is poor. The eyes are small, as are the olfactory organs, thereby enhancing the need for an efficient lateral-line system. In juveniles, where the lateral-line system is not yet well developed, the eyes and olfactory organs are relatively much larger. Free-living male *Linophryne* have developed tubular eyes.

Angler fishes will eat fish, squids, crustaceans, arrow worms or any other life form they can attract. The stomach is remarkably elastic. A specimen of *Linophryne quinqueramus* 3.5in (8.9cm) long contained: a deep sea eel (*Serrivomer*) 1.3in (3.3cm) long, a deep sea Hatchet fish (*Sternoptyx*) 1in (2.5cm) long, two bristle mouths (*Cyclothone*) 1–2.5in (2.5–6cm) long and five shrimps 0.5–1.2in (1.2–3cm) long.

To help the prey into the stomach, and keep it there, the long, curved teeth of the globular female ceratioids are depressible. They give way to allow the food to pass down and then spring back to prevent its escape. In *Neoceratias spinifer* the longest teeth originate on the outside of the jaws. *Lasiognathus* has the upper jaws expanded as a flap on each side with the teeth pointing outwards until the flaps are closed down over the lower jaw.

It is thought that in species in which the illicium is short, and only moves from the vertical to the horizontal, ie is scarcely retractable, once the prey is near either a sudden lunge or buccal suction is used to secure the meal.

In some of the ceratioids and oneirodids the illicium is so long that the lure can be placed far in front of the mouth and then slowly retracted as the unsuspecting prey appears.

Gigantactis has a very thin, whip-like illicium several times the body length emanating almost from the tip of the snout. In what manner and for what purpose this small-mouthed species uses it are unknown.

A logical development of the retractable illicium is shown in *Thaumatichthys*. This is a somewhat flattened species of angler known only from a very few specimens. Its illicium is short and its luminous two-lobed esca hangs down from the roof of the mouth. It swims around slowly or, as it is rather flattened, may lie on the bottom with its mouth open. Any prey that approaches the esca is already in the mouth and the jaws merely have to close gently around it. KEB

Representative genera of angler fishes. (1) *Edriolynchus* (3in, 8cm). (2) *Melanocoetus* (5.5in, 14cm). (3) *Gigantactis* (6in, 15cm). (4) *Lasiognathus* (3in, 7cm). (5) *Thaumatichthys* (3in, 8cm). (6) *Linophryne* (3in, 7cm).

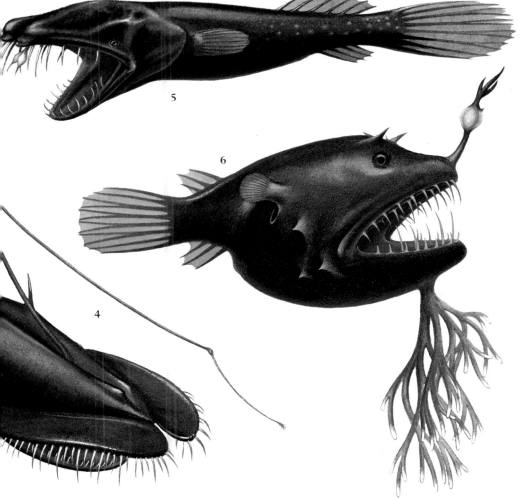

A Self-fertilizing Hermaphrodite
Reproduction strategies in angler fishes

Some of the deep-sea angler fishes reproduce in a manner unique among vertebrates. Deep-sea ceratioid angler fish lay and fertilize their eggs in deep water, after which the eggs float up to the surface. In some species the eggs are very numerous. A 2.5in (6.3cm) long *Edriolynchus* had over 9,000 eggs and a 26in (65cm) long *Ceratias holboelli* carried nearly 5 million immature eggs. (It has been suggested that the absence of a swim bladder makes more room for eggs.)

When the eggs hatch the larvae are, in the case of *Himantolophus groenlandicus*, about 0.1in (2mm) long. Even at this stage the sex of the larva is apparent because on the snout of the females is a small bud that will develop into the illicium. The larvae feed and grow in the surface waters. In the North Atlantic most species spawn in summer. The linophrynids, however, spawn in spring and their larvae live in deeper water (330–660ft, 100–200m). The larval phase lasts about two months and as the fishes grow they go deeper. A rapid metamorphosis then occurs; they change into subadults, looking more like their parents as sexually different characters become apparent.

By the time of metamorphosis the non-parasitic male has already developed large testes. Although his jaws are rather feeble pincer-like structures, he carries on feeding and grows very slowly. He is sexually mature at this small size, but the female is not mature for years after metamorphosis. Then she may be up to 20 times the length of her mate (according to species). When the breeding season arrives the male nips hold of the female's skin with his pincer-like jaws. Fertilization of the eggs is effected and the cycle starts again. *Himantolophus* and *Melanocoetus* are two genera believed to use this system.

The reproductive strategy of parasitic males is the most remarkable among vertebrates and, indeed, is the only known example of complete vertebrate parasitism.

After metamorphosis only the females feed. The male again has pincer-like teeth but is unable to eat even small food items. As a result of larval feeding he has a thick gelatinous layer which is believed to act as a food reserve until he finds a female. If he fails to find a mate before the reserve runs out he dies. For the good of the species, many more males hatch than females. How the male finds the female is not certain, but as he still has well-developed eyes and olfactory organs there must be clues for him to follow. How he finds a female of the same species will be discussed below. In contrast to the previous system, the male's testes are not developed. On meeting a female the male bites her skin—anywhere—and the two bodies fuse. The male loses most of his organ systems and becomes little more than a sac containing testes which do not develop until the female so dictates. He is fed by the nourishment in the female's blood *via* a placenta-like arrangement. Discharge of his sperm is presumably under the control of hormone levels in the female's blood. More than one male may attach to a female. By incorporating the male as part of her body, the female has developed into a self-fertilizing hermaphrodite. The mechanism of this fusion has aroused some interest in those working on problems of tissue rejection in humans.

In at least two genera, the oneirodid *Leptacanthichthys* and *Caulophryne*, both free-living males with developing testes and parasitic males have been found. Similarly, females with maturing ova but without attached males have been caught. It seems that these two taxa display "facultative parasitism" (ie some individuals have opted to be parasitic).

How do the males identify their own species and do they ever make mistakes? The answer to the last part of the question is "rarely." Hundreds of ceratioid anglers have been caught and there is only one known mistake, where a male *Melanocoetes* was latched on to, but not fused with, a female *Caulophryne*. It was mentioned above that the eyes and nostrils of the males are probably involved. Doubtless a female will exude a particular scent to which the male is sensitive. Correlated with the eye development is the fact that the structure and shape of the esca (the luminous organ at the end of the illicium) are specific to each species, so it is likely that they act as a lighthouse for the male.

▶ **At her command,** two parasitic male angler fish fused to the body of a female (*Edriolynchus schmidti*).

▼ **The metamorphosis of a deep-sea angler fish** (*Ceratias holboelli*). (1) An unmetamorphosed male with a thick gelatinous skin. (2) An unmetamorphosed female. The beginning of the illicium can be seen above the eye. Unmetamorphosed angler fish are normally found near the surface of the ocean. Metamorphosis occurs at a depth of about 3,300ft (1,000m). (3) A metamorphosed male. Note the pincer-like teeth and the absence of an illicium. From this time on males do not eat. (4) A young metamorphosed female with a well-developed illicium. (5) An adult female with an attached parasitic male. The largest known male was about 6in (15cm) long, the largest female nearly 6.5ft (2m).

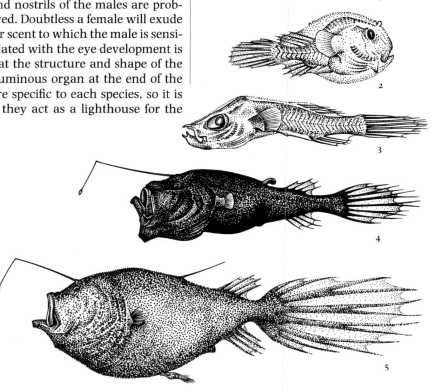

The light is produced by bacteria in the central bulb of the esca. Beneath the thin skin is a thick layer of connective tissue with nerve fibers. Then there is a dark layer and inside that a highly reflective layer. The central part is hollow and has glandular cells (to feed the bacteria?), blood vessels, and at the middle are the luminous bacteria.

The presence of nerves has led to speculation that the esca may be sensitive to touch. The light in ceratioids is yellowish-green or bluish and has been found to shine in a series of flashes.

The esca is a lure for prey as well as a mate. The light from the chin barbel of *Linophryne* is produced by chemical means.

Each organ is like a tubercle with a lens surrounded by blood vessels. Inside are the light-producing cells (photocytes) and loops of capillaries. Light production is controlled by oxygen in the blood stream. In the laboratory the addition of hydrogen peroxide to the organs will produce light.

KEB

SILVERSIDES, KILLIFISHES...

Series: Atherinomorpha
Superorder: Acanthopterygii.
About one thousand species in about 165
genera, 21 families, 2 orders and 1 division.

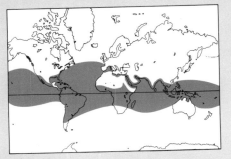

Silversides
Division: Atherinoidei
Two hundred and forty species in 50 genera
and 7 families.
Distribution: worldwide, fresh and sea waters.
Size: maximum length 24in (60cm).
Families: Atherinidae, including the **grunion**
(*Leuresthes tenuis*); Bedotiidae;
Dentatherinidae; Isonidae; Melanotaeniidae;
Telmatherinidae; Phallostethidae.

Killifishes
Order: Cyprinodontiformes
Six hundred species in 80 genera and
9 families.
Distribution: pantropical and north temperate
regions in fresh and brackish waters.
Size: maximum length 12in (30cm).
Families: Anablepidae, including **quatro ojos**
(genus *Anableps*); Aplocheilidae;
Cyprinodontidae; Fundulidae; Goodeidae;
Poeciliidae, including **guppy** (*Poecilia reticulata*),
mosquito fish (*Gambusia affinis*); Profundulidae;
Rivulidae; Valenciidae.

Ricefishes and their allies
Order: Beloniformes
One hundred and sixty species in 35 genera
and 5 families.
Distribution: worldwide, fresh and sea waters.
Size: maximum length 3.3ft (1m).
Families: **flying fishes** (family Exocoetidae),
halfbeaks (family Hemiphamphidae),
needlefishes (family Belonidae), **ricefishes**
(family Adrianichthyidae), **sauries** (family
Scombersocidae).

▶ **Moonlighting grunion.** The best-known
example of a fish that synchronizes its
spawning behavior with lunar cycles is that of
the grunion of the North American Pacific
coast. This is a marine species that moves
inshore and spawns in the sand of beaches at
night, following the highest of the spring tides
after both the new and full moons. As the
waves roll in the fish come ashore and deposit
and fertilize their eggs in the wet sand near the
top of the high-tide mark. The eggs are
normally hidden about 3in (8cm) below the
surface INSET LEFT. The eggs develop in the
sand, awaiting the next set of spring tides, some
12–14 days later. Then the eggs hatch INSET
RIGHT and the young are washed into the sea.

F ISH that fly, fish that give birth to live
young, fish used to control mosquitoes
and fish that spawn to the cycles of the
moon: these are some of the unusual life-
styles found in the series Atherinomorpha.
Some of its members are extremely well
known, thanks to their wide use in experimental studies of embryo development and
their adaptability to aquarium conditions.
The series comprises some 1,000 species of
minute to medium-sized fishes distributed
worldwide in temperate and tropical
regions, inhabiting fresh, brackish and sea
water. Here it will be described as consisting
of three groups: silversides, killifishes, and
ricefishes and their allies.

The silversides are not placed in a separate named order because at present no
uniquely derived characteristics are
recognized that set apart these seven
families from all other teleosts. Silversides
are characterized by having a silvery lateral
band at midbody, hence their common
name, but this character is found in many
other groups of fishes. Most silversides are
narrow-bodied and elongate, though some
are relatively deep-bodied, such as species of
the genus *Glossolepis* of New Guinea, which
are used as food fish.

Many atherinomorphs have a prolonged
development time with fertilized eggs taking
one week or more to hatch, as opposed to
the more usual time in teleosts of from one
to two days. The grunion, a species of silver-
side found on the West Coast of North
America from southern to Baja California,
is well known because of its spawning
behavior which is correlated with the lunar
cycle. Grunion spawn during spring tide;
the fertilized eggs are stranded during low
tide, and hatching is stimulated by the
waters of the returning high tide two weeks
later.

Silversides, such as species of the North
American genus *Menidia* found in coastal
and gulf drainages, are used as bait fish.
Another common name for silversides is
smelts, though they are not related to the
true smelts of the salmoniform family
Osmeridae.

The killifishes are probably best known to
the public at large by fishes in the family
Poeciliidae. Included here are the guppy,
certainly one of the most common domestic
animals, and the mosquitofish, which consumes mosquito larvae and pupae and so is
used throughout the world as a mosquito-
control agent. Poeciliids are also of great
interest to biologists because populations of
some species occur composed entirely, or
almost entirely, of females. One such species,

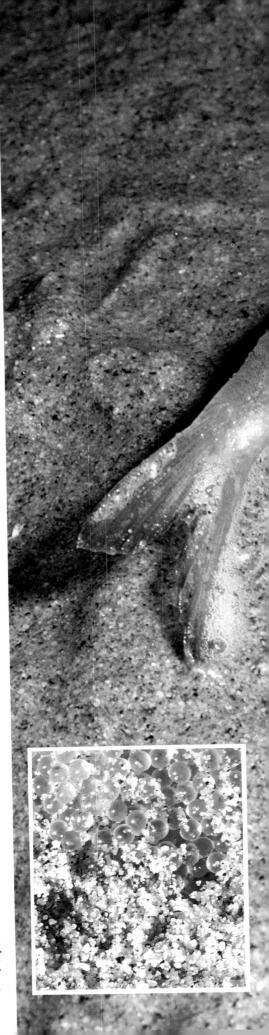

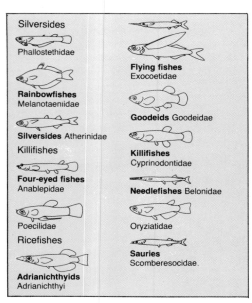

▲ **Outlines of representative families** of silversides, killifishes, ricefishes and their allies.

◄ **A popular aquarium fish,** the Red rainbow fish (*Glossolepis incisus*) from Lake Sentani in Irian Jaya in Indonesia. (Male in foreground.)

► **A Goldie River rainbow fish** (*Melanotaenia goldiei*) from Papua New Guinea.

▼ **The Mosquito fish** from Mexico has been introduced elsewhere to control mosquitoes.

Poecilia formosa, reproduces by spawning with males of another poeciliid species which do not contribute genetic material to the offspring but simply stimulate development of the egg.

Other killifishes or killies in the Old and New World tropical families Aplocheilidae and Rivulidae, respectively, are also popular aquarium fishes, as well as pest-control agents. Their popularity as aquarium fishes is no doubt in part due to their bright and beautiful coloration, as well as to their hardy nature, which is so well known that hobbyists often exchange fishes around the world by mailing them, wrapped only in a plastic bag with a little water and air and shipped in an insulated container. Included in these two tropical families are the annual killifishes, which are so named because adults rarely live longer than one rainy season, at the end of which time they spawn, leaving fertilized eggs in the drying muddy substrate. The eggs spend the dry season buried in the mud, lying quiescent until the rains return the following season. When the rains begin again the eggs are stimulated and hatch and the cycle is repeated.

North American killifishes are less brightly colored, as are most temperate fishes, but no less well known, at least to biologists. The mummichog, a species found in brackish water, from Canada to the southern USA, is widely used in experimental embryological studies. Its biology is probably better known than that of any other species of bony fish.

Some of the most spectacular killifishes are those of the genus *Anableps*, found from southern Mexico to northern South America. These are the largest killifishes, some reaching to over 12in (30cm). They are certainly most well known by the characteristic from which their common name of quatro ojos or "four eyes" is derived. Each eye is divided horizontally into two sections: there are separate upper and lower corneas and retinas. *Anableps* species are usually found just below the surface of the water, and seen from above only by the tops of their eyes which protrude above the surface. The upper eyes are used for vision above the water, whereas the lower eyes are used for vision below.

Killifishes of the families Poeciliidae, Anablepidae, and the Goodeidae of the Mexican plateau and western North America, all have species that are viviparous (ie there is internal fertilization of females by males, and females subsequently give birth to live young). The males of viviparous species within these families have anal fins that are modified for sperm transfer—the first few anal rays are generally more elongate and elaborate than those in the rest of the fin and are modified into what is called a gonopodium. At one time it was believed that all viviparous killifishes formed a natural group, ie they were more closely related to each other than any was to a group of oviparous or egg-laying killifishes. This has been found not to be the case, with egg-laying killifishes often judged to be more closely related to a particular viviparous group. This knowledge of killifish relationships has led us to understand that viviparity, although characterized by many

complex anatomical and behavioral modifications, is a way of life that has arisen several times within the evolution of killifishes.

The order Beloniformes comprises two groups, the ricefishes (Adrianichthyoidei) and the halfbeaks, flying fishes, needlefishes and sauries (Exocoetoidei).

All ricefishes are contained in one family. They are so-called because they were discovered in Oriental rice paddies. The scientific name of the common ricefish genus *Oryzias* is in fact derived directly from the name of the rice plant *Oryza*. Ricefishes are common in fresh and brackish waters from the Indian subcontinent throughout coastal Southeast Asia into China, Japan and along the Indo-Australian archipelago into the Celebes (Sulawesi).

Members of the halfbeak family are freshwater and marine fishes characterized by a very elongate lower jaw and a short upper jaw, hence "half a beak." Most halfbeaks are oviparous, but some, such as the Indo-Australian *Dermogenys pusillus*, have internal fertilization and are viviparous.

Species in the family of flying fishes do not exhibit true flight as the name implies. They have expanded pectoral (and sometimes pelvic) fin rays that allow them to glide for several seconds after they propel themselves above the water surface.

In the needlefish family species have an elongate upper as well as lower jaw—they are more or less fully beaked. The common name is a reference to the extremely sharp, needlelike teeth in the jaws. Most of the cosmopolitan temperate and tropical needlefishes are marine whereas some, such as *Potomorhaphis guianensis* of the Amazon, live in fresh water. Needlefishes are characterized by having bones, and also often muscle tissue, that are rather greenish in color. This does not, however, prevent them from being used as a food fish.

Sauries are commercially among the most important beloniform fishes. *Cololabis saira*, found in both the eastern and western Pacific, is an important species in fisheries in Japan. The scientific name *Scomberesox*, the type genus in the family, is a composite of *Scomber*, a name for mackerels, and *Esox*, the name for pikes and pickerels. Apparently sauries appeared to early workers as having characteristics of those two distantly related groups—five to seven finlets behind the dorsal and anal fins being reminiscent of the mackerels and the moderate-sized jaws with strong teeth being much like those of pikes and pickerels.   LP

SPINY-FINNED FISHES

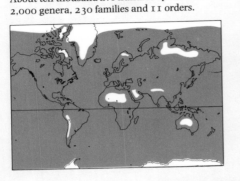

▶ **Zebrafishes** ABOVE live in coastal waters of
the Indo-Pacific Ocean. Their graceful
elongated fin rays bear extremely poisonous
spines. Their genus (*Pterois*) contains four or
five similar species (family Scorpaenidae, order
Scorpaeniformes).

▶ **Outlines of representative species** BELOW of
spiny-finned fishes.

▼ **This mosaic-like fish** is *Cleidopus glorimaris*,
an Australian pineapple fish (order
Beryciformes) with a multitude of common
names. Like the other members of the family
Monocentridae it has a covering of large spiny
scales on its deep rounded body. It has two open
pits beneath the chin which contain luminous
bacteria.

THE superorder Acanthopterygii contains
the latest flowering of bony fish evolution, some 60 percent of all living fishes
divided into two series. The earliest forms
referable to the group are found in the Cretaceous period (135–65 million years ago).
The common name alludes to the presence
of spines either in front of the soft dorsal fin
(although this also occurs independently in
other taxa, for example notacanths, see
p44), or incorporated into the anterior part
of the dorsal fin, or as a separate first dorsal
fin. Anal fin spines occur similarly and
spines in the ventral fins are widespread.
However, with such a successful, dominant
and species-rich group any or all of these
spines have been secondarily lost or modified in many species. The presence of rough-
edged (ctenoid) scales is another superficial
character of spiny-finned fishes but, again,
these have been modified into a wide array
of scutes or plates, or have even been lost.
There is also a tendency for the pelvic fins
to move forward on the body compared with
other superorders. The difficulty of dis-
tinguishing between basal acanthopterygians and paracanthopterygians has been
exemplified with regard to the status of
Polymixia on p94.

By far the major group of the spiny-finned
fishes are the Perciformes—the classical
"perch-like" fishes, whose classification is
very debatable (see p118). However, within
the rest of the spiny-finned fish there are a
number of discrete, well-defined orders.

The Beryciformes (with some nine families) are large-headed, deep-water marine
fishes found in all temperate and subtropical
oceans. Most families have rough scales, but
the family Monocentridae, with only two
species, has been given the graphic common
name pine-cone fishes. These rounded little
fish (of which *Monocentrus japonicus* is the
best known) live in small schools in the
Indo-Pacific Ocean. The body is covered
with irregular bony plates and the soft-
rayed dorsal fin is preceded with a few large,
alternately angled spines. The pelvic spines
are massive and erectile. Although pine-
cone fishes do not grow to more than 9in
(23cm) long, they are commercially viable in
Japan, where they are eaten. They have two
small luminous organs under the lower jaw
with colonies of bacteria providing the light.
Their novel appearance coupled with
luminosity has made them popular aquarium fishes in the Far East.

Luminous organs are also present under
the eye in members of the family Anomalopidae. Each organ is a peculiar flat white in
daylight but at night glows with a blue-
green light. The luminous organs blink on
and off when functioning and are controlled
by rotating the entire gland. These are
shallow-water fishes living among the coral
reefs of both the East and West Indies. They
are of no commercial importance although,
if caught, the luminous gland is removed
and used as bait in subsistence fisheries.

The family Berycidae contains mid-water,
large-eyed species with compressed bodies.
Most species are red or pink. The flesh is
excellent and, in the North Atlantic at least,
commands a good price when offered at
markets.

Species belonging to the other families are
poorly known. Many have fine spines on the
head and anterior part of the body, especially when young. This once led to the
adults of *Anoplogaster cornuta* being known
as *Caulolepis longidens*. Despite the difference
in appearance between juveniles and adults
the mistake was realized when intermedi-
ates were found. However, as the young
were described first the former name
remains in use.

The order Zeiformes comprises deep-
bodied, extremely compressed fishes. The
John Dories (the European *Zeus faber*, the
American *Zeus ocellata*) are North Atlantic
fishes with a lugubrious appearance. They
have extremely protrusile jaws and feed on
small fishes and crustaceans. The origin of

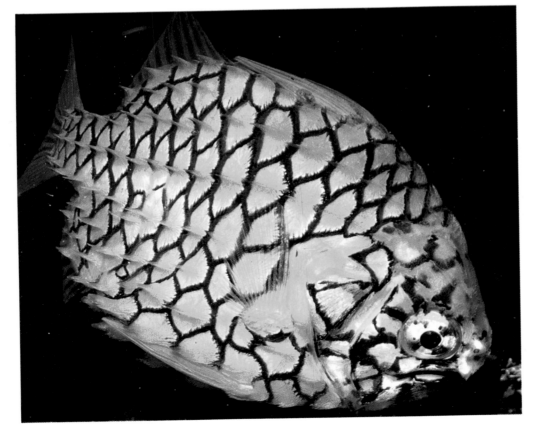

fin, ctenoid scales, spines on the head and pelvic fins well forward). The order contains over 20 families including the gurnards, the extremely poisonous stone fishes of Australasia and the armored sea robins and pogges.

Species of the family Cottidae are common in fresh water. The large head of *Cottus gobio* has given it the name bullhead in the United Kingdom. In North America they are called sculpins. A closely related family, the Cottocomephoridae, is endemic to the deepest lake in the world, Baikal in Siberia. Here, because the lake is capable of supporting life down to the bottom (in other deep lakes the lower waters are deoxygenated), a whole series of "deep-sea" freshwater fishes has evolved. Although luminosity has not been developed, many of the cottocomephorid characteristics parallel those of deep-sea fishes. *Cottocomephorus comephoroides* is a species of the open sea living down to depths of 3,300ft (1,000m) in summer. In winter they live closer to the bottom, but usually in shallower water.

The **flying gurnards** (order Dactylopteriformes) are not gurnards and probably do not fly. They are heavily built, bottom-living fish with a heavy, bony skull. The pectoral fins are greatly expanded into colorful fans and may well serve to frighten away potential predators.

The Red Breast of the Three-spined Stickleback

It is probably for its breeding behavior that the Three-spined stickleback is best known. The male, in his breeding dress of red breast and bright blue body, is well known to children as a prized tiddler to be caught in spring. The male builds a roughly spherical nest from strands of water plants stuck together by secretions from his kidneys. The choice of site varies and, oddly, there is some evidence that males with more bony scutes prefer a sandy locality while those with fewer plates a muddier one. The males' bright colors serve both to advertise the nest site to the female and to warn other males to keep away. An attracted female is courted, shown the nest, and, if she approves, lays her eggs there. More than one female may be induced to lay. The

fertilized eggs are guarded by the male who fans them and removes diseased eggs. During the parental phase the male changes to an inconspicuous dark livery. As the eggs hatch, the male progressively destroys the nest and, a few days after hatching, the young are left on their own. KEB

Another order with large pectoral fins is the **sea moths** (Pegasiformes). They are small, tropical marine fishes with a body encased in bony scutes and variously developed snouts. There are probably only six species. Because of their curious shape, and the fact that the shape is maintained when the fish is gutted and dried, they are often sold as curios in the Far East. Apart from the fact that they are egg-layers and eat very small bottom-living invertebrates, little is known about their biology.

Some of the problems with classification were mentioned in the introduction. Here we have a practical example. The families included in the group of **sticklebacks and pipefishes** (including seahorses, shrimp fish, flute mouths and some without common names), are now known not to constitute a natural assemblage. Despite superficial similarities, ie bony scutes, isolated spines before the dorsal fin, and some elongation of jaws, which led to the association, there are three quite distinct units. Therefore, ere too long, this order will cease to exist in its present form.

The "humble" stickleback is found in most fresh, brackish and sometimes coastal waters throughout Eurasia and northern America. It is highly variable in form. Although mostly "three-spined" two- and four-spined individuals occur. There are populations in Canada that never have pelvic fins. Freshwater forms usually have fewer bony scutes than brackish or marine forms. Generally, sticklebacks never grow to more than 3in (7.5cm) long but in lakes in the Queen Charlotte Islands, off the coast of British Columbia, there are dark pigmented forms that grow to 8in (20cm) long. Both the abundance and variability of this fish have led to extensive studies of its behavior

as well as to various distinctive forms having formerly been accorded status as individual species.

The Fifteen-spined stickleback is a solitary species most of the year but it also makes a nest of seaweeds. The Nine-spined stickleback (which usually has 10 spines) has at most only a few small scutes. It is nearly as widespread as the Three-spined but rarely enters brackish or saline waters. Two genera are confined to northern America: the Brook stickleback (usually with 5 spines) which is fairly widespread and may even be found in coastal waters of reduced salinity in the north, and the Four-spined stickleback which only occurs in the northeastern part of northern America.

Despite the presence of protective spines on the back and in the pelvic fins, sticklebacks form an important part of the food chain and are eaten by larger fish, birds and otters. Even so, there was a report of cleaning symbiosis between a three-spined stickleback and a pike.

nently in fresh water. Important unifying characters of these fish are long snouts with a small terminal mouth, the elongation of the first few vertebrae (in the shrimp fish, the first six vertebrae form over three-quarters of the length of the vertebral column) and the peculiar structure of the first dorsal fin which, when present, consists not of fin rays but of prolonged processes associated with the vertebrae.

The shrimp fishes have an extremely compressed body entirely enclosed in thin bony sheets. Only the downturned posterior part of the body is free, to allow tail-fin movement for locomotion. They live in shallow warm seas, sometimes among sea-urchin spines where they shelter for protection. The Deep-bodied snipe fish lives in deeper water and is covered with prickly denticles and a row of scutes on the chest. Apart from the lack of parental care, little is known of their reproductive behavior.

The pipefishes, however, show a remarkable series of reproductive adaptations. The simplest strategy, in the subfamily of nerophiine pipefishes, is for the eggs to be loosely attached to the abdomen of the male. A more elaborate condition is present in some syngnathines where the eggs are individually embedded in spongy tissue covering the male's ventral plates. Further protection in other groups is provided by the development of lateral plates partially enclosing the eggs. In all cases it is the male that carries the eggs.

The seahorses, which are merely pipefishes with the head at right angles to the body, a prehensile tail and a dorsal fin adapted for locomotion, exhibit the ultimate in egg protection. The trend seen in the development of protective plates is continued until a full pouch (or marsupium) is formed, with a single postanal opening. The female has an ovipositor by which the eggs are placed in the male's pouch until the pouch is full. Apparently this simple act is not always done without mishap.

Hatching time varies with temperature, the young leaving the pouch between 4 and 6 weeks after the eggs were deposited. In some larger species, the male helps the young to escape by rubbing his abdomen against a rock, in others there are vigorous muscular spasms which may expel the young with considerable velocity. After "birth" the male flushes out his brood sac by expansion and contraction to expel egg remains and general debris to prepare for the next breeding season. This may occur relatively soon as three broods a year are not unknown.   KEB

▲ **Hanging around,** a school of shrimp fish (*Aeoliscus strigatus*), members of the order of sticklebacks and pipefishes.

◄ **Highly variable coloration** ABOVE is a feature of *Hippocampus kuda,* a seahorse widespread in Indo-Pacific coastal regions. Although often offered for sale in aquarium shops they are hard to keep in captivity as it is difficult to provide their diet of very small live fish and invertebrates.

◄ **In the warm southern oceans** lives *Solenostomus paradoxus,* a relative of the seahorses and pipe fishes. It is about 3in (8cm) long and cryptic. The female (seen here) has cape-like pelvic fins which form a pouch. Within this the eggs are attached to short filaments. When they hatch the young become independent immediately.

The tube snouts are primitive relations of the stickleback found in the cooler waters either side of the North Pacific. The American species *Aulorhynchus flavidus,* which resembles the European Fifteen-spined stickleback, lives in huge shoals. No nest is built but the female lays sticky eggs along the stipe of the giant kelp (large seaweed) which is first bent over and then glued down. The male defends the eggs. Its Japanese relative *Aulichthys japonicus* is poorly known but is reputed to lay its eggs inside a seasquirt (*Cynthia*).

The seahorses, and their relatives the pipefishes, flute mouths, shrimp fish and snipe fish, are an almost entirely marine group; only a few pipefishes live perma-

Shooting Down Insects

Some members of the perciforms have evolved elaborate techniques for catching prey. Six species of archer fish are popular with aquarists; they occur naturally in both fresh and salt water from India and Malaysia to northern Australia. The name archer fish is rather inappropriate as it really *spits* droplets of water to catch its prey. The archer fish has a groove in the roof of the mouth. The tongue is thin and free at the front but thick and muscular with a mid-line fleshy protuberance at the back. When the tongue and fleshy protuberance are pressed against the roof of the mouth, it converts the groove into a narrow tube. The thin, free end of the tongue acts as a valve. When the archer fish spots a "juicy" insect, the tongue is pressed against the roof of the mouth, the gill covers are jerked shut and the tip of the tongue is flicked shooting out the drops of water. Archer fish are able to compensate for refraction of light by placing the body vertically below the prey. A fully grown fish can shoot down an insect from up to 5ft (1.5m) whereas babies can only shoot a few inches without loss of accuracy. Results of experiments with adult archer fish suggest that their aim may be quite haphazard and the "shooting down" of an insect is due to massed firepower rather than sharp shooting. It seems that when the archer fish is only a few inches from the insect it will jump out of the water and snatch the insect with its jaws rather than shoot it down. Archer fish often frequent murky water where they are found cruising just below the surface.   BB

▲ **On target,** *Toxotes jaculator,* one of the species of archer fish, from Java.

▶ **Free food for the taking**—a grouper feeding on a shoal of small fish.

No other order of fishes approaches that of the **perch-like fishes** in number of species and variety of form, structure and ecology. The perciformes comprise the largest vertebrate order, containing over 150 families embracing about 8,000 species. Whether the perch-like fishes form a natural (monophyletic) assemblage is debatable. At present the perciforms are ill-defined and lack a single specialized character or combination of characters to define the group.

The most "typical" members of the perciforms are the species in the perch family. The perch body is typically deep and slender; the two dorsal fins are separate; the pelvics are near the "throat" and the operculum ends in a sharp, spine-like point. They are adapted to northern hemisphere temperatures; warm winters retard the maturing of sperm and eggs.

The European perch is a sedentary species, preferring lakes, canals and slow-flowing rivers. The ruffe or pope of Europe and southern England is a bottom-feeding species, frequenting canals, lakes and the lower reaches of rivers. Confusingly it has contiguous dorsal fins.

The zander is a native of eastern Europe that has been introduced to Britain on numerous occasions from the 19th century onwards. Its British distribution is patchy, notably the River Ouse and other slow-flowing Cambridgeshire rivers and some Bedfordshire lakes, but it is apparently extending its range. The North American zander (or walleye) occurs naturally in wide, shallow rivers and lakes.

The North American darters are the most speciose percids with nearly 100 species. The common name is derived from their habit of darting between stones, as they are bottom-dwelling fishes that lack swim bladders. While many species of darter are brightly colored, the Eastern sand-darter is an inconspicuous translucent species, usually found buried in sandy stream beds with only the eyes and snout protruding.

Like that of all other teleosts, the percid skeleton is basically bone, with some cartilage, though the skeletons of the perciform families of louvars and ragfishes are largely cartilaginous. The louvar, the only species in its family, is probably related to the mackerels and tunas. It lives in tropical seas, grows to about 6ft (1.8m) and has a tapering, pinkish colored body. Its pectoral fins are sickle shaped; the pelvics minute; its dorsal and anal fins are long, low and set far back on the body. The louvar feeds on jellyfish; consequently its intestine is very long, with numerous internal projections which increase the absorbent surface area of the gut. The significance of the cartilaginous skeleton remains a mystery.

The two species of ragfishes are so called because they appear to be boneless and look like a bundle of rags that has been dropped on the floor. Little is known of their biology. The Fantail ragfish grows to 18in (45cm) and has a deep, laterally compressed scaleless body with small spines on the lateral line and fins. The Brown ragfish grows to some 7ft (2.1m). Its body is elliptical and lacks scales, spines and pelvic fins. It is apparently eaten by Sperm whales.

The large spotted groupers are voracious predators. Sometimes they are found with black, irregular lumps, either lying in the body cavity or bound by tissue to the viscera: these are mummified sharp-tailed eels. Each eel is swallowed by the grouper and in its death throes punctures the gut; it gets squeezed into the body cavity where it becomes mummified.

The Queensland grouper, a native of Australian seas, may weigh up to half a tonne and is another sea bass with a hearty appetite! This fish has been known to stalk pearl and shell divers, much as a cat stalks a mouse, a habit that has led to stories of divers being swallowed by groupers.

The barracudas are another group of perciforms reported to attack divers. They are tropical marine fish which in some areas, especially the West Indies, are more feared than sharks. The body is elongate and powerful; the jaws are armed with sharp, dagger-like teeth. Barracudas eat other fish and seemingly herd shoals, making the food easier to catch. Large individuals tend to be solitary, but younger barracudas aggregate in shoals. The barracuda makes very good eating but is notorious for being sporadically poisonous due to the accumulation of toxins acquired from the fish on which it feeds.

The mackerels, tunas and bonitos or scombrids are also delicious perciforms. The scombrids are mainly schooling fishes of the open seas, cruising at speeds of up to 30mph (48km/h). Their bodies are highly streamlined, terminating in a large lunate caudal fin. Some scombrids have slots on the dorsal surface of the body in which the spiny dorsal fin fits to reduce water resistance. Behind the dorsal and anal fins are a series of finlets, the number of which varies according to the species. In all species the scales are either very reduced or absent.

The Common mackerel is found on both sides of the North Atlantic. On the European side it ranges from the Mediterranean to Ireland. It is a pelagic fish which in summer

The Mystery of the Swordfish

The swordfish is the only species in its family. It is also a solitary fish, and may weigh up to 1,500lb (675kg). The snout is produced into a powerful, flattened sword. Swordfish live in all tropical oceans but will enter temperate waters, occasionally straying as far north as Iceland.

The sword has a coat of small denticles similar to those found on sharks. Its function is unknown but suggestions include its use as a weapon (ie the swordfish strikes a shoal of fishes with lateral movements afterwards devouring the mutilated victims) and as extreme streamlining with the snout acting as a cutwater.

There are numerous accounts of large fish attacking boats, but often there is no attempt to discriminate between swordfish, spearfish and sailfish, all of which have similar habits. There is no doubt that a swordfish could pierce the bottom of a boat and have the sword snap off in its struggles to withdraw it. In the British Museum (Natural History) there is a sample of timber which a swordfish snout has penetrated to a depth of 22in (56cm). It is also reported that the ship HMS *Dreadnought* sprang a leak on voyage from Ceylon (Sri Lanka) to London. Examination of the hull revealed a 1in (2.5cm) hole punched through the copper sheathing which was reputed to have been made by a swordfish. Periodically swords are found in whale blubber. Whether these attacks on ships and whales are deliberate remains unresolved. The most likely explanation is that when a swordfish, which can travel at speeds up to 60mph (100km/h), encounters a boat or whale it finds it impossible to divert in time and a collision becomes inevitable.   BB

forms enormous shoals at the water's surface near coasts to feed on small crustaceans and other plankton. In winter the shoals disband and move to deeper water, where the fish approach a state of hibernation.

The skipjack tuna is a cosmopolitan marine species that owes its name to its habit of "skipping" over the surface of the water in pursuit of smaller fish.

The swordfish and the family of sailfishes, spearfishes and marlins (istiophorids) are all fast-swimming fishes closely related to the scombrids (see box). The istiophorids include some of the world's most popular marine sport fishes and are often referred to as billfishes, a term also used, confusingly, for the swordfish. In cross-section the bills of these fish are rounded and they have two ridges on each side of the caudal peduncle, as opposed to just one in the swordfish. Several billfish species are known to be migratory, possibly to follow food. Billfishes are fish-eaters; they erect the dorsal fin to prevent prey escaping. They can also use the bill as a club to maim their victims as they rush through a school of preferred fishes, such as the Frigate mackerel.

Marlins lack the pelvic fins present in the sailfish and spearfish. Their classification is unresolved. The only easily identifiable species and probably the largest is the Indo-Pacific Black marlin whose pectoral fins are permanently and rigidly extended.

Sailfishes undergo a remarkable change during their larval development. Larvae of about 0.3in (9mm) have both jaws equally produced, armed with conical teeth; the edge of the head above the eye has a series of short bristles; there are two long pointed spines at the back of the head; the dorsal fin is a long, low fringe and the pelvic fins are represented by short buds. At 2.4in (6cm) it begins to resemble the adult: the upper jaw elongates, the teeth disappear, the dorsal fin differentiates into two fins, the spines at the back of the head become reduced and the bristles disappear. Young swordfish also undergo a similar series of changes.

The scats are found in Southeast Asia, Australia and eastern Africa. At about 0.75in (1.7cm) they start to resemble the adult; before this they are very different. The larval phase is known as the "Tholichthys" stage because the famous ichthyologist Albert Günther failed to recognize the young and described them as a separate genus, *Tholichthys*.

Scats are primarily marine but range into brackish or fresh water, adjusting very rapidly to waters of different salt levels. It is still unknown how scats can regulate their body salts so rapidly, but however they manage it, they can cross sea water concentration gradients that are lethal to over 90 percent of other teleosts.

Closely related to and having a similar larval stage as the scats are the butterfly fishes. Butterfly fishes are exquisitely colored

How Tuna Fish Keep Warm

Tunas differ from other scombrids and all other teleosts in their ability to retain metabolic heat *via* a countercurrent heat-exchange system which operates in the muscles and gills. Red muscle occurs in large proportions in tunas. It is extremely vascular, so the muscle cells are supplied with oxygen- and carbohydrate-enriched blood, enabling them to utilize a highly efficient, aerobic metabolism. Aerobic metabolism liberates energy to drive the muscle and heat, which is retained in the body by the countercurrent heat-exchange system. White muscle is found in large proportions in all other fish. White muscle has a very poor blood supply and carbohydrate is metabolized anaerobically, which liberates just enough energy to drive the muscle.

Fishes normally lose heat through their gills during respiration but the tunas' countercurrent heat-exchange system ensures that the metabolic heat is returned to the body. The advantage to the tunas is twofold, the muscles operate at a higher temperature, helping the fish to achieve high speeds and allowing it to range further north.

BB

▲ **Where impairment is best sustained** TOP. Butterfly fishes have a dark stripe to disguise their eyes and a false eye on the dorsal fin to minimize the effects of predation. They live around coral reefs. This is the Filament butterfly fish (*Chaetodon auriga*).

▲ **Unexpected attractiveness.** Many of the wrasses (family Labridae) are both large and brightly colored. In some species there are marked differences in color and pattern between the sexes. They live in shallow areas of the oceans worldwide except for colder regions. This is a Purple queen (*Mirolabrichthys tuka*).

and move with a flitting motion. They are distributed worldwide in warm waters around coral reefs. Despite their bright coloration, the pattern camouflages the eye and it is difficult for a potential predator to distinguish the head from the tail. Many species have a dark vertical bar that runs through the eye, further disguising it, and to add to the confusion many species also have an eye spot near the caudal fin. Butterfly fishes delude would-be predators by swimming slowly backwards. Once the predator lunges at the eye spot, the butterfly fish darts forwards, leaving its attacker rather confused. The Indo-Pacific butterfly fish known as the forceps fish is so called because its snout is extremely long and used like a pair of forceps to reach deep into reef crevices.

Included by some workers in the butterfly fishes family are angelfishes, distinguished from butterfly fishes by their larger, rather rectangular bodies and heavy spines at the base of the gill cover. The Blue angelfish has a dark blue ground color broken by a series of narrow, curved white stripes with a similarly marked caudal fin. Some years ago a specimen appeared in a Zanzibar market with the caudal fin lines broken, resembling Arabic characters reputed to read *Laillaha, Illalahah* ("There is no God but Allah") and the other side *Shani-Allah* ("A warning sent from Allah"). Blue angelfish are normally sold for a few cents; this fish eventually fetched some 5,000 rupees.

The surgeonfishes are another family of reef-dwelling fishes which, during development, have a larval or "acronurus" stage where the larvae are totally dissimilar from the adult. There are almost 1,000 species of oval-bodied surgeonfishes. The name alludes to a razor-sharp, lancet-like spine on either side of the caudal peduncle. In most species the spines lie in a groove and are erected when the fish is disturbed or excited. The spines are a formidable weapon, inflicting slash wounds into the victim, as the surgeonfish lashes its tail from side to side. The unicorn fish has a large lump on its head and has two immovable spines on either side of the caudal peduncle.

Surgeonfishes do not school but travel in small groups using their small incisor-like teeth to scrape plants and animals from reefs and rocks. Frequently surgeonfishes show variation in color—the Yellow surgeon has yellow and gray-brown color phases. The Common surgeonfish, found in the Atlantic, changes from blue-gray to white anteriorly and dark posteriorly when chasing another member of the species in territorial disputes.

In the Indo-Pacific surgeonfishes are a tasty food fish but the offending caudal peduncle is cut off prior to sale.

Members of the family of stargazers are widely distributed in warm seas and earn their name from their eyes which are set on top of the head so that they appear to be staring at the sky. Stargazers have electric organs situated just behind the eyes which deliver a shock sufficient to stun small fish—which are then eaten. The European stargazer is common in the Mediterranean; it grows up to 1ft (30cm) and has flaps of tissue in the mouth that resemble worms, tempting potential prey to approach. Predators are deterred from eating the stargazer by grooved spines situated above each pectoral fin. At the base of the spine is a poison gland; as the spine inflicts a wound, poison is trickled into it via the groove. Stargazers are usually found buried in the sand, with only the eyes and snout tip protruding.

Some perciforms sometimes form unusual

relationships with other vertebrates and invertebrates and even with floating objects! The remoras or shark-suckers are slim fishes usually associated with sharks, large fishes and occasionally turtles. Their dorsal fin is modified into a sucking disk, the rim of which is raised, and the platelike fin rays can be adjusted to create a strong vacuum between the disk and a remora's chosen partner. It is unknown what benefit such an association is to either the remoras or the animals to which they attach. It has been suggested that remoras are simply "hitching a ride," a phenomenon known as phorecy, or that they associate with sharks to feed on the scraps they can snatch from the shark's meal. Remoras have been observed entering the mouths of manta rays, large sharks and billfishes, hence it has been mooted that they may fulfill a role like that of cleaner fish. However, there is no documented evidence of remoras undertaking cleaning duties. Occasionally, fairly large remoras (*Echeneis naucrates*) have been found in the stomachs of Sand sharks (*Odontaspis taurus*).

Despite their usual attachment to sharks, remoras are competent swimmers and often leave the "host" to forage. When free-swimming in a group, remoras arrange themselves with the largest on top, smallest at the bottom, reminiscent of a stack of plates. The group swim in a circular fashion; it seems remoras do not like to swim unaccompanied.

Ancient legend has it that remoras can impede the progress of sailing vessels, even stop them. The remora is also reported to have magic powers and a potion including one was supposed to delay legal proceedings, arrest aging in women and slow down the course of love!

Pilot fishes in the family Carangidae also associate with sharks and rays. It was thought that the pilot-fishes guided the sharks to their prey and in return received protection from their enemies by their proximity to such a formidable companion. Sharks and rays are in fact seeking food, and although the pilot-fish gain from the hunting efforts of sharks they never lead the foray. Pilot-fish never stray too close to the shark's mouth but they have been seen to take refuge in the mouths of rays that do not eat fish.

The young of another carangid, the common Horse mackerel, shelter in the bell of the sombrero jellyfish (*Cotylrhiza*). Why these small fishes do not get stung is unexplained but possibly lack of glutathione (an amino acid that stimulates release of sting

cells) in their mucus coats protects them.

Members of two other families also associate with jellyfish. Young butterfishes are laterally compressed fish which lack pelvic fins and shelter under the protection of the Portuguese man-of-war (genus *Physalia*). The closely related Nomeidae are known as "man-o'-war" fishes and are distinguished from the preceding family by the presence of pelvic fins. Again, it is unknown how these fish gain immunity from the stinging cells of this jellyfish.

Among the family Gobiidae, fishes in the genus *Evermannichthys* habitually live inside sponges. The bodies of these little fishes are slender and nearly cylindrical, allowing them easy access to the larger orifices on the sponge's surface. Scales are either absent or poorly developed, but along the lower posterior line of the sides are two series of large, well-separated scales whose edges are produced into long spines. A further series of four spined scales is situated in the middle line, behind the anal fin. It is thought that these structures are used by the fish for climbing up the inner surfaces of the sponge cavities.

Another Indo-Pacific genus of goby, *Smilogobius*, is commensal with a snapping shrimp. The goby is usually found at the

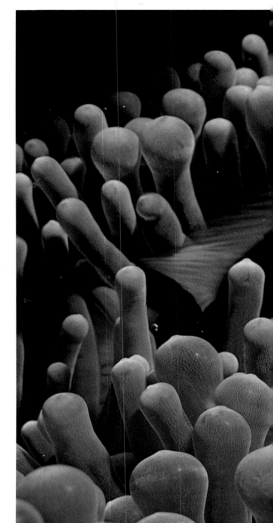

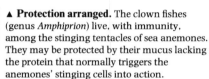

▲ **Protection arranged.** The clown fishes (genus *Amphiprion*) live, with immunity, among the stinging tentacles of sea anemones. They may be protected by their mucus lacking the protein that normally triggers the anemones' stinging cells into action.

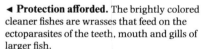

◄ **Protection afforded.** The brightly colored cleaner fishes are wrasses that feed on the ectoparasites of the teeth, mouth and gills of larger fish.

► **Protection taken.** Blennies (family Bleniidae) are found worldwide, mostly in shallow seas. Here a blenny takes refuge in a brain coral.

▼ **Protection desired,** remoras following a ray.

burrow entrance while the snapping shrimp busily excavates it. When danger threatens, the goby dives into the burrow; this also alerts the shrimp which follows the fish inside. The snapping shrimp will not emerge until the goby is once again on sentry duty at the burrow entrance.

The five species of the family of clown-fishes are small, brightly colored fishes of warm shallow seas where they live in association with large sea anemones. The relationship is intimate: the clownfish remain inside the anemone when it with-draws its tentacles. The clownfish benefit by protection from predators so they never stray far from their anemones, but the latter can happily exist without the clownfish. Probably the clownfish feed on particles stolen from the tentacles of anemones. It is unknown whether the anemones' sting-cells are lethal to nonsymbiont fishes. If they are then the clownfishes' immunity to their sting is also unexplained. Current views are that the toxin of the sting-cells is mild and the clownfishes' mucus coat is sufficient pro-tection, or that the mucus coat lacks glutathione which triggers the sting-cells.

The Cardinal fish lives among the spines of certain long-spined sea urchins. The urchins do not benefit from the relationship, but the Cardinal fish gains protection from its partner's spines. Another cardinal fish (*Astropogon stellatus*) is only 2in (5cm) long and common in the Caribbean and lower Florida coasts. This fish is found in either the mantle cavity of giant conch shells or the inner cavities of sponges. The host gains little benefit from the association but the cardinal fish gains protection from predators.

A centrolophid rudder fish (*Schedophilus*) has formed the curious habit of accompany-ing logs, planks, barrels, broken boxes and other flotsam, which has earned it the title "wreck fish." The rudder fish gains shelter and feeds on barnacles and other inverte-brates which live on the flotsam.

A number of species of wrasse (*Labroides*) have an unusual "cleaning" relationship with other fishes: they remove ectoparasites and clean wounds or debris. There are some 600 species in the wrasse family, usually nonschooling, brilliantly colored and found on reefs in all tropical and temperate marine waters. The wrasses have well-developed "incisor" teeth which protrude like a pair of forceps from a protractile mouth and which in noncleaning species are used for removing fins and eyes of other fishes.

The cleaner fishes are small, brightly-colored reef dwellers that occupy a specific area, the "cleaner station." Their diet is mostly parasitic organisms on the bodies and gills of fishes. The association between cleaner and customer is not permanent. Fishes requiring "cleaning" congregate at the cleaning stations and follow a specific behavior pattern that invites the cleaner to get to work. The customer allows the cleaner to move all over the body, including such sensitive areas as the eyes and mouth, and even to enter the branchial cavity to remove parasites from the gills. The cleaners benefit by immunity from predation during the cleaning and presumably at other times, since many of the customers are predators on fishes the size of these wrasses.

A feature common to many wrasses is their ability to burrow and usually to sleep buried in sand. Nearly 50 species of Hawaiian labrids sleep buried in the sand at night. The exceptional labrid (*Labroides phthirophagous*) secretes a mucous night-shirt around itself.

The parrotfishes family is closely related to the wrasses and some species (eg *Pseudoscarus guacamia*) secrete a mucous nightshirt that surrounds the whole body. This mucous cocoon may take up to half an hour to secrete and as long for the fish to release itself. Interestingly this cocoon is not secreted every night but only under certain conditions, the causal factors of which are a mystery. It seems that the mucous cocoon may be a protective device, preventing odors from the parrotfishes reaching predatory fish, eg moray eels.

Species in the family of grunts are pretty, tropical marine fishes that have earned their name from the noise they produce by grinding together well-developed pharyngeal teeth. Grunts are deep-bodied fishes that usually travel in schools. Several reef-dwelling species indulge in a form of kissing. Two individuals approach with their mouths wide open and touch lips. The behavior is reminiscent of the "kissing gouramis" and is thought to play a role in courtship.

Members of the drums family are rather dull-colored fishes—they also derive their name from the noise they produce. The noise is caused by muscles vibrating the swim bladder, not always attached directly thereto but running from either side of the abdomen to a central tendon situated above the swim bladder. Rapid twitches of the muscles vibrate the swimbladder walls which have a complex structure and act as a resonator to amplify the drumming sound. A swim bladder is absent in the drum genus *Menticirrhus* so this fish produces only a weak noise by grinding its teeth.

Species in the leaffishes family rely on crypsis (pretending to be something else) to catch their food. They are found in tropical fresh waters in Africa, Southeast Asia and South America. The Southeast Asian leaf-fishes are very perchlike—none mimics leaves and the body is only slightly com-pressed. The most common leaffish of this area is *Badis badis* (sometimes placed in a family of its own, Badidae) which has a large number of different color forms and is found in streams of India and Indochina. The most spectacular leaffishes are those found in South America. These are deep-bodied fish with soft dorsal fin rays: they closely resemble floating leaves in both contours and marks—even a "leaf stalk" is present, emanating from the lower jaw. Leaffish usu-ally hide beneath rocks or in crevices, where they look like a dead leaf that has become wedged, then dart out to capture prey. The most famous leaffish (*Monocirrhus polyacan-thus*) is found in the Amazon and Rio Negro basins of South America. Its body is leaf-shaped and tapered towards the snout, with an anterior barbel mimicking a leaf stalk. The fish reaches about 4in (10cm) in length and is a mottled brown similar to dead leaves. It drifts with the current and on approaching a potential meal the leaffish bursts into action and assisted by its large protrusile mouth engulfs fishes up to half its size.

A perciform family with one of the largest numbers of species is that of the cichlids. They are also very popular aquarium fishes.

▲ **An assembly of cardinals.** There are many species of cardinal fishes—small, brightly colored shoaling fish of tropical and temperate seas. Most species are reef dwellers in the Indo-Pacific Ocean.

▶ **Extractive industry.** Parrot fishes (family Scaridae) have teeth fused into a "beak" with which they bite off lumps of living coral. Large grinding teeth in the throat then chew the coral to extract the food. The limestone residue is excreted.

◀ **A couple of cichlids** involved in premating behavior. Members of the family Cichlidae live in South America, Africa, parts of southwest Asia and India. Most species are territorial and display parental care of the eggs and young. The great rift-valley lakes of Africa have produced cichlids with extremely specialized feeding habits, such as scale-scraping, eye-eating and snaffling young from a parent's mouth. The South American species shown here (the Butterfly cichlid, *Papiliochromis ramirezi*) is a more generalized feeder.

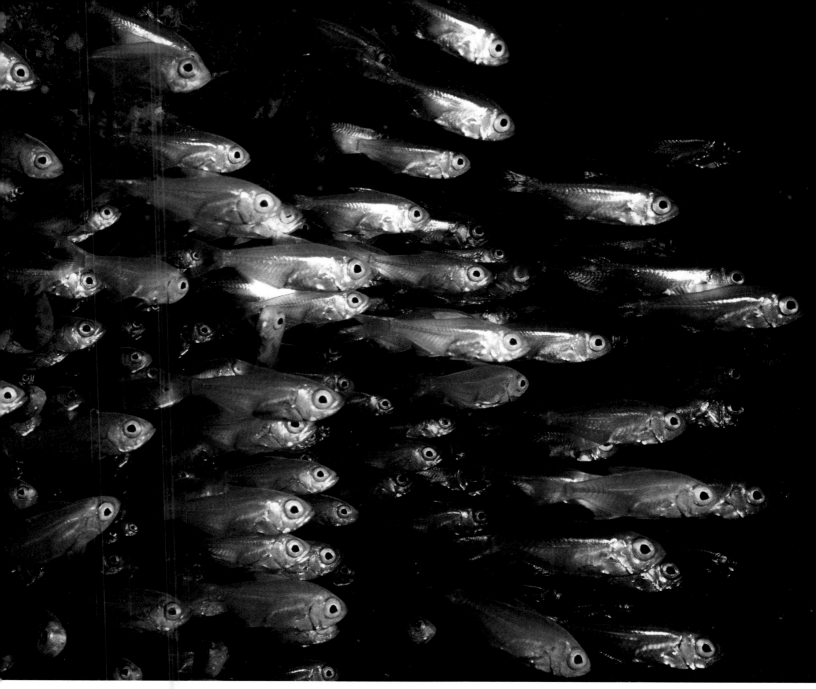

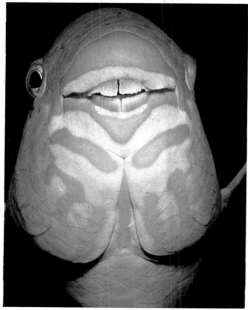

They are characterized by a single nostril on each side of the head and two lateral lines on each side of the body. The pharyngeal bone is triangular, lying on the floor of the "throat"; its function is to break up food against a hard pad at the base of the skull, and it is of diagnostic importance in the identification of species.

Cichlids are widely distributed in Central and South America, Africa, Syria, Madagascar, southern India, Sri Lanka and Iran. There are at least 1,000 species, over half of which are found in Africa, especially the Great Lakes, Victoria, Malawi and Tanganyika, each of which boasts 100 or more endemic species.

Cichlids have evolved all kinds of dentition to cope with their varied diet. Vegetarians have bands of small notched teeth in the jaws, sometimes with an outer chisel-like series for cutting weed or scra-

ping algae off rocks. Fish-eating species have large mouths armed with strong pointed teeth for securing struggling fish. The mollusk-eating varieties have strong, blunt pharyngeal teeth to grind up mollusks, although in some species the lateral jaw teeth are modified, enabling the fish to remove the snail from its shell before swallowing it. Finally, in some species the dentition is greatly reduced and deeply embedded in the gums of a very distensible mouth. These species feed almost entirely on the eggs and young of mouth-brooding cichlids which they force the parent to "cough up." In Lake Barombi, Cameroon, there is a genus of cichlid (*Pungu*) whose diet consists entirely of freshwater sponges.

In the rapids of the lower Zaïre river there lives an unusual cichlid, *Lamprologus lethops*. The head of this fish is rather flattened, its body nearly cylindrical and the eyes are

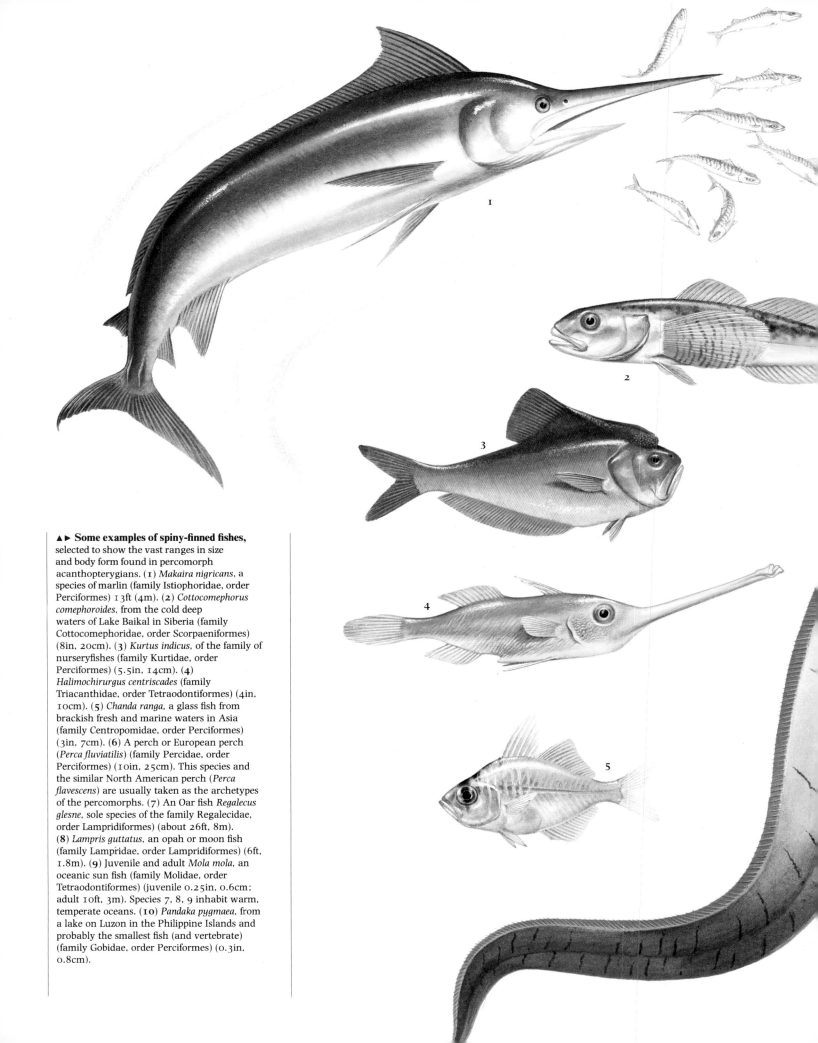

▲▶ **Some examples of spiny-finned fishes,** selected to show the vast ranges in size and body form found in percomorph acanthopterygians. (**1**) *Makaira nigricans*, a species of marlin (family Istiophoridae, order Perciformes) 13ft (4m). (**2**) *Cottocomephorus comephoroides*, from the cold deep waters of Lake Baikal in Siberia (family Cottocomephoridae, order Scorpaeniformes) (8in, 20cm). (**3**) *Kurtus indicus*, of the family of nurseryfishes (family Kurtidae, order Perciformes) (5.5in, 14cm). (**4**) *Halimochirurgus centriscades* (family Triacanthidae, order Tetraodontiformes) (4in, 10cm). (**5**) *Chanda ranga*, a glass fish from brackish fresh and marine waters in Asia (family Centropomidae, order Perciformes) (3in, 7cm). (**6**) A perch or European perch (*Perca fluviatilis*) (family Percidae, order Perciformes) (10in, 25cm). This species and the similar North American perch (*Perca flavescens*) are usually taken as the archetypes of the percomorphs. (**7**) An Oar fish *Regalecus glesne*, sole species of the family Regalecidae, order Lampridiformes) (about 26ft, 8m). (**8**) *Lampris guttatus*, an opah or moon fish (family Lampridae, order Lampridiformes) (6ft, 1.8m). (**9**) Juvenile and adult *Mola mola*, an oceanic sun fish (family Molidae, order Tetraodontiformes) (juvenile 0.25in, 0.6cm; adult 10ft, 3m). Species 7, 8, 9 inhabit warm, temperate oceans. (**10**) *Pandaka pygmaea*, from a lake on Luzon in the Philippine Islands and probably the smallest fish (and vertebrate) (family Gobidae, order Perciformes) (0.3in, 0.8cm).

completely covered by skin and tissues of the head. It is further distinguished from other species of *Lamprologus* by its small scales and lack of pigment. The eyes are thought only to be able to perceive light but do not form visual images. In such fast-flowing water eyes would probably be of little benefit and easily damaged and so they are reduced in this "blind" cichlid. The species is currently known from only a few dead specimens, so details of its biology remain a mystery.

Also found in the same Zaïre rapids is *Mastacembelus brichardi* (family Mastacembelidae), a spiny eel. The eyes of this species are minute, deeply embedded in the head and covered by expanded jaw muscles. Its body is more or less depigmented, so is a milky white or pinkish color. Once again little is known of the biology of this species.

"Like a fish out of water" is an ill-quoted expression as a number of fish are quite at home out of the water. Many of the spiny eels are air-breathers and utilize this ability to survive in poorly aerated water or mud. Like many species of spiny eel, *Macrognathus aculeatus* spends the daytime in a mud burrow, excavated by rocking and forward-wriggling movements that submerge it at a constant rate, leaving only the tips of the nostrils protruding.

The mudskippers, of the goby genus *Periophthalmus*, are found in tropical Africa and spend a great part of their time walking or "skipping" about mangrove roots at low tide. During these periods the branchial chamber is filled with water and oxygen exchange continues over the gills. When the oxygen in this water is exhausted the mudskippers replace it with oxygenated water from a nearby puddle. The mudskippers can also respire through the skin (cutaneously) and have a highly vascular mouth and pharynx through which gaseous exchange can take place; they are therefore often seen to sit with their mouths gaping.

Mudskippers are very competent amphibious fishes. Their pectoral fins are highly modified and the membraneous part is carried at the base of a highly muscular "stump" that can be moved backwards, forwards and sideways. Movement is achieved by "crutching." The mudskipper swings the pectorals forwards while the weight of its body is supported by the pelvic fins. Then, by pressing downwards and backwards with the pectorals, the body is both lifted and drawn forwards. At the end of the movement the body falls and rests again on the pelvic fins. Rapid movement is achieved by curling the body to one side and

 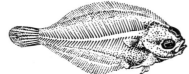 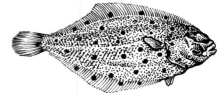

suddenly straightening it, "flipping" itself distances up to 2ft (60cm). Mudskippers can also skitter across the surface of the water in a series of jumps as well as swim normally when submerged.

When the tide returns most of the mudskippers retreat into elaborate burrows with enlarged living chambers in the mud, over which they are highly territorial. Those mudskippers that do not possess burrows, usually juveniles, spend most of their time out of the water, and are obliged to climb surrounding mangrove trees as the incoming tide brings with it numerous other predatory fish.

The Anabantidae and Ophiocephalidae are two more perciform families renowned for their ability to breathe atmospheric air. The anabantids include the climbing perch, the Kissing gourami and the genus of Siamese fighting fish. They are also called labyrinth fishes for their labyrinth-like accessory breathing organ. The accessory breathing organs are housed at the top of each gill chamber; they are hollow and formed from highly vascular skin lining the gill chambers. As the fish grows the organs become more convoluted, increasing the surface area available for respiration. The anabantids rely on atmospheric air for survival and quickly suffocate if denied access to the surface of the water.

The gouramis are tropical freshwater fish found from India to Malaya. The Kissing gourami is found in the Malay Peninsula and Thailand. The name is derived from the broad-lipped mouths by which two individuals approach each other and appear to be kissing. This apparent affectionate gesture is in reality a threat, issued in exercise of territorial rights or mate selection.

The Siamese fighting fish that are so brightly colored in aquaria are an unexciting brownish red color in the wild. The highly colored varieties are obtained by selective breeding, a process by which characters potentially present in wild forms are encouraged to develop in captivity by breeding those individuals which demonstrate the required character most strongly.

The snakehead family is closely related to the anabantids but contains long cylindrical fishes with flattened, rather reptilian-looking heads. These fish inhabit rivers,

ponds and stagnant marsh pools in Southeast Asia. The various species of snakehead differ in the extent to which each has developed the habit of breathing air. The accessory breathing organs are simpler than those found in anabantids, consisting of a pair of cavities lined with a vascular thickened and puckered membrane. These lunglike reservoirs are not derived from the branchial chambers but are pouches of the pharynx.

The snakeheads are also able to move overland but do so by a rowing motion of the pectoral fins. During prolonged drought snakeheads survive by burying themselves in mud and aestivating; in hot dry weather they become torpid.

The examples of perciforms given are a small representation of the amazing diversity of this group as it is currently recognized.

The origin of **flatfish** is obscure; fossils are known from the Eocene epoch (54–38 million years ago) but these are as specialized as the living species. There are about 500 extant species divided into seven families (Psettodidae, Citharidae, Scophthalmidae, Bothidae, Pleuronectidae, Soleidae and Cynoglossidae). The members of the most primitive family, Psettodidae, have rather perch-like pectoral and pelvic fins; only the eyes and long dorsal fin distinguish them from the sea-perch, suggesting that flatfish evolved from perch-like ancestors.

All adult flatfish are bottom-living fish but their eggs, which contain oil droplets, float at or near the sea surface. The larvae take a few days to hatch; the fish appear symmetrical, with an eye on each side of the head and a ventrally situated mouth, further suggestive of their perch-like ancestry. When about half an inch (1cm) long a metamorphosis occurs which has profound effects on the symmetry of the skull and the whole fish. The changes are initiated when one eye migrates across the head to lie alongside the other, its passage being assisted by resorption of the cartilaginous bar of skull separating them. The nostril simultaneously migrates to the eyed or colored side. Except for the psettodids, the mouth also twists into the same plane as the eyes. In the soles (genus *Solea*) the mouth twists unusually onto the blind side. The eye that migrates is often characteristic of

▲►▼ **A change of direction.** Flatfish start life as normally shaped fish with an eye on each side and a horizontal mouth. As the larva grows ABOVE one eye migrates to the other side of the head and the mouth twists until the adult comes to lie permanently on one side. The consequent disformation in the adult can be seen in this photograph of a plaice RIGHT. Adult flatfish are adept at adapting the color of their pigmented side to match that of the surrounding seabed—see the flounder BELOW. Although they are normally bottom-dwellers some species, for example the large halibut (genus *Hippoglossus*) which grows to over 6.5ft (2m) can swim actively and catch fish in midwater.

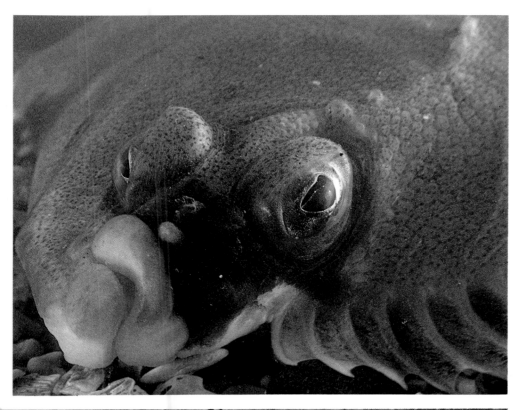

particular families. Members of the family Bothidae are called left-eyed flounders because their right eye usually migrates, so the uppermost, colored side is the left one. Pleuronectidae are right-eyed flounders because ultimately the right side is uppermost. In the psettodids equal numbers are found lying on either side.

While these radical changes are taking place the little fish sinks to the sea bottom. Flatfish do not have a swim bladder, so they remain lying at or near the bottom, on their blind side. The body shape of adult flatfish is quite variable—the European turbot and its relatives are nearly as broad as long, whereas the tongue soles are long and narrow. Frequently, flatfish bury themselves, by flicking sand or by wriggling movements of the body, leaving just their eyes and upper operculum exposed. There is a special channel which connects the gill cavities. Water is pumped from the mouth over both sets of gills, but the expired water from the gills on the buried side is diverted through the channel and expired from the exposed side.

Many flatfish are predominantly brown on the colored side, although they often have spots and blotches of orange thus enabling them to blend with the substrate. The pleuronectids, however, are masters of disguise among fish as they can change their color to match the substrate. When placed on a chequered board some species can reproduce the squares with reasonable accuracy. The American flounders can even produce an effective camouflage on colored backgrounds, although their attempts at reproducing reds are inaccurate.

All flatfish are carnivorous but their methods of catching prey are quite diverse. Members of the family Bothidae are daytime hunters that feed on other fish. They swim actively after their prey and have very acute vision. Species belonging to the families Soleidae and Cynoglossidae hunt at night for mollusks and polychaete worms which they locate by smell. These families of flatfish both have innervated filamentous tubercles instead of scales on the blind side of the head which probably enhance their sense of smell. The pleuronectids are intermediate: some, eg the halibut, actively prey on fish, others, eg plaice, hunt polychaete worms and crustacea, relying on smell and visual acuity to locate their prey.

The majority of flatfishes are marine, but a few species can live in sea or fresh water. The European flounder frequently migrates up rivers to feed and is found up to 40mi (65km) inland in the summer, returning to spawn in the sea in the fall. The American flatfish *Achirus achirus* is a freshwater species, often kept by aquarists. It has a large surface area to weight ratio and can suspend itself by surface tension at the water surface. It can also "stick" itself to rocks or the sides of aquaria by creating a vacuum between the underside of its body and the substrate.

There is no obvious difference between the sexes in most species of flatfish, although in the scald-fish genus the male has some filamentous dorsal and pelvic fin rays. The males in the closely related genus *Bothus* have spines on the snout, their eyes are wider apart than the females' and the upper rays of the colored side pectoral fin are elongate.

Judging by their worldwide distribution the flatfish are apparently a very successful group of fish. They are found from the Antarctic to beyond the Arctic circle. In temperate regions flatfish are represented in enormous numbers and have become commercially exploited. In the North Atlantic, food fishes, eg plaice, have been so intensively fished that they are farmed to replenish natural stock.

The tetraodontiformes are an order of mostly marine fishes that have the teeth fused into a beak. Among their number are poisonous fishes, inflatable fishes, and one of the largest oceanic teleosts. None has scales; instead they are covered either with spines or with skin so thick that little can penetrate it.

The group of marine fishes called triacanthoids derives its name (meaning three-spined) from the presence of a conspicuous spine in the first dorsal fin and from the spine that forms each pelvic fin. Rarely, there is a small fin ray behind the pelvic spine. The group is widespread in the Indo-Pacific Ocean, largely in shallow waters, and a few species occur in the tropical West Atlantic.

Very little is known of the biology of triacanthoids. Some species have massive teeth and remains of hard-shelled mollusks and crustaceans have been found in the stomachs. They are of no great significance to humans. A few species inhabit deeper waters and even less is known about them than about shallow-water species. This is a pity because they are so bizarre that their life style invites much speculation. *Halimochirurgus* has a long, slender, upcurved snout that may form half of the body length. The mouth is terminal, faces upwards and has just a few small, widely spaced teeth. The fish lives over mud flats and sand beds and is presumed to feed on worms. *Macrorhamphosodes* has a slightly

shorter but wider and straighter snout. The lower jaw has well-developed stocky teeth but those on the upper jaw are few and feeble. Most remarkable, however, is that as the fish grows, the mouth twists to the right or the left.

The trigger fishes are named for the interlocking "trigger-like" mechanism of their first and second dorsal fin spines; the small second spine must be released before the larger first spine can be depressed. Triggers, with their bony scales, have an easily recognized overall appearance, with their opposite and almost symmetrical dorsal and anal fins actively undulating as the major propulsion mechanism. Many have striking color patterns and are inhabitants of coral reefs. The file fishes are a group of elongated balistids with very small, rough scales. The dorsal spines are much further forward than in the trigger fishes. They have extremely small mouths and feed by picking up small invertebrates. Many have an expandable dewlap between the chin and the anal fin, a feature taken to extremes by *Triodon bursarius* (see below).

The box fishes or cow fishes have been described as bony cuboid boxes with holes for the mouth, eyes, fins and the vent. Some

The diodontids are exclusively marine and have larger spines than the tetraodontids. This latter family has the "beak" in each jaw in separate halves. Some tetraodontids live in fresh water. *Tetraodon mbu* is a striking black and yellow species widespread throughout the Zaïre system and some other West African rivers. This, and some of the other African freshwater species, are occasionally kept in aquaria, but they are aggressive inhabitants. Tetraodontids can inflate themselves with water and also by gulping air. It is difficult to evaluate the survival value of the latter technique because they float upside down at the surface where they are attacked by birds. All are, however, very poisonous fishes but, despite that, some are valued as a delicacy. Particularly in Japan, the more poisonous parts are eaten as *fugu*, and are prepared by specially trained cooks. Even so, death by poison from ill-prepared *fugu* is not unknown.

The family Triodontidae contains only one species, the rare and poorly known *Triodon bursarius*, which is found throughout the Indo-Pacific Ocean. The lower jaw has a single beak-like tooth but the upper jaw beak is in two separate halves. The extensive, thin dewlap is not expandable as in file fishes, but can be pulled forwards by the pelvic fin skeleton which forms its anterior edge. The function of this flap is unknown.

The oceanic sunfishes are the giants of the order. *Mola mola* is the largest species, probably weighing up to 2,200lb (1,000kg). Seen from the side this browny-blue fish is nearly circular, with the caudal fin reduced to a mere skin-covered fringe, but with the dorsal and anal fins produced into "oars" used for locomotion. It is most often seen lying on its side at the surface, allegedly basking but probably dying. A rare film of a young specimen alive shows that it swims rapidly in an upright position by vigorous sculls of the expanded fins. The diet consists of jellyfish and other small, soft items. Below the scaleless skin is a very thick layer of tough gristle. Although not common, *Mola mola* lives worldwide in tropical and subtropical waters. In common with the related genus *Masturus*, the Sharp-tailed sunfish, the young are spherical and have long spines on the body which become reduced and lost as the adult shape is developed. The last genus in the family, *Ranzania*, is more elongated. It is also a more colorful species—deep blue on the back paling ventrally, with diagonal black-edged silver stripes on the sides. Like its few close relatives, it is found worldwide in warmish waters. BB/KEB

▲ **Set in a monochrome world** this is a species of file fish (*Oxymonacanthus longirostris*), sometimes known as the Beaked leatherjacket. It has erectile dorsal spines (not visible here) and lacks scales. It lives in the West Pacific and East Indian Ocean on the deep side of coral reefs and belongs to a group whose members grow to only 3–4in (8–10cm). Many file fishes are brightly colored. (Order Tetraodontiformes.)

◄ **Barbed fish.** The aracanids or cowfish come from the South Pacific. They have rounded bodies and a remarkable series of scythe-like spines along the sides and back of the carapace (that is the shield along the back). In some species the male has a hump on the snout and his color may differ from that of the female. (Order Tetraodontiformes.)

▼ **A prickly precaution.** Porcupine and puffer fishes can inflate themselves as a means of defending themselves against or deterring predators. When so inflated, either with water or air, the lateral spikes of the scutes stick out.

species also have two small, horn-like processes over the eyes, hence cow fish. The rigid outside skeleton (exoskeleton) is formed by fused bony scutes. Box fishes are slow-swimming, brightly colored fishes of shallow tropical seas. In case their armor should be thought inadequate against predators, box fish can also secrete a virulent toxin if molested. There are about 50 species, none of which grows to more than 2ft (60cm); most are shorter than 1ft (30cm).

Aracanids are commonest in the South Pacific and look like ovoid versions of box fishes armed with a series of curved or scythe-like spines. They are brightly colored and, like the box fishes, the coloring may differ between sexes.

The puffer fishes (diodontids) derive their main common name from having the body covered in spines which rise from their normal flat position when the body is inflated as a defense tactic.

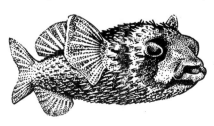

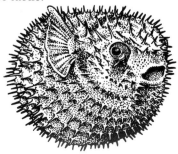

COELACANTH, LUNGFISHES, BICHIRS

Orders: Polypteriformes, Coelacanthiformes; superorder: Ceratodontimorpha
Probably seventeen species in 6 genera, 4 or 5 families and 4 orders.

Bichirs or polypterids

Order: Polypteriformes
Probably ten species in 2 genera of the family Polypteridae.
Distribution: fresh waters in Africa.
Size: maximum length about 3.3ft (1m) but most are smaller.
Genera: **bichirs** (*Polypterus*), **Reed fish** (*Erpetoichthys calabaricus*).

Coelacanth

Order: Coelacanthiformes
Family: Latimeriidae.
Sole species *Latimeria chalumnae*.
Distribution: around the Comoro Islands.
Size: maximum length 5.9ft (1.8m).

Lungfishes

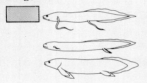

Superorder: Ceratodontimorpha
Six species in 3 genera, 2 or 3 families and 2 orders.
Distribution: fresh waters of Brazil, Paraguay, Africa and Queensland, Australia.
Size: maximum length 6.5ft (2m).

▶ **Strange fish of uncertain affinity** ABOVE.
Polypterids live only in the fresh waters of Africa. There is no certainty as to which other group of fish they should be related. They are active predators and also have the ability to survive a long while out of water.

▶ **The last of a famous line.** The anachronistic coelacanth only became known to science in 1938. Between the Devonian and Cretaceous periods (400–65 million years ago) they lived worldwide. Today they are found only off the Comoro Islands in the western Indian Ocean.

THREE disparate groups of fishes are linked together here solely on the grounds that all are anachronistic. Although the term "living fossils" has been applied to them, such a description, apart from being a contradiction in terms, does not help our understanding of their relationships. "Anachronistic" is a much more useful term and also reflects the truth.

The **bichirs** are endemic to the fresh waters of Africa. The family contains just two genera, the true bichirs with nine species and the Reed fish. To which other major group of fishes the bichirs are related is a source of much debate. Almost every group has been suggested at one time or another during the last century.

Bichirs are primitive-looking fishes. They have thick, diamond-shaped scales that articulate by a "peg and socket" joint, gular plates, and the upper jaw fixed to the skull. As a group they retain a surprising number of primitive features. Their fossil record is scanty, the oldest known remains coming from deposits of the Cretaceous period (135–65 million years ago). All the fossils are in Africa, largely within the present area of distribution.

True bichir species owe their generic name (*Polypterus*, "many fins") to the row of small finlets on the back, each finlet consisting of a stout spine supporting a series of rays. The pectoral fin has a stout, scale-covered base. Although the tail is symmetrical in appearance, its internal structure retains the primitive, upturned, heterocercal condition.

Bichirs live in sluggish fresh waters. Their swim bladders have a highly vascularized lining that is used as a lung, enabling them to live in deoxygenated waters. The young have external gills. They are largely nocturnal fishes, not known for an active lifestyle. At night they feed on smaller fishes, amphibians or large aquatic invertebrates. Within Africa they are confined to the tropical regions in drainages emptying into the Atlantic Ocean or the Mediterranean. Living birchirs rarely grow to more than 2.5ft (75cm) long but, to judge from the size of the scales, some fossil species might have been twice as long.

The Reed fish is a slender, eel-like version of the true bichirs. It lacks pelvic fins and the subsidiary rays on the isolated spines. A much smaller species, it is found only in reedy areas in coastal regions of West Africa near the Gulf of Guinea. It appears to eat mostly aquatic invertebrates.

Fossil **coelacanths** first appeared in rocks of the Devonian period (400–350 million years ago) and continued to occur until about 70 million years ago when, along with the dinosaurs, they disappeared from the fossil record. Since the coelacanth was discovered in 1938 and again in 1952 (see box) over a hundred have been transferred to scientific institutions but, although its anatomy has been detailed, little is known of its biology and its relationships are still an unresolved controversy. Indeed, in a symposium volume published by the California Academy of Sciences in 1979 there are several contradictory papers each advocating different groups of fishes as the closest relatives of the coelacanth.

Much of the biology of the coelacanth has to be inferred from its anatomy and catching records. No specimens have been kept alive for long.

Apart from the mysterious first catch, all

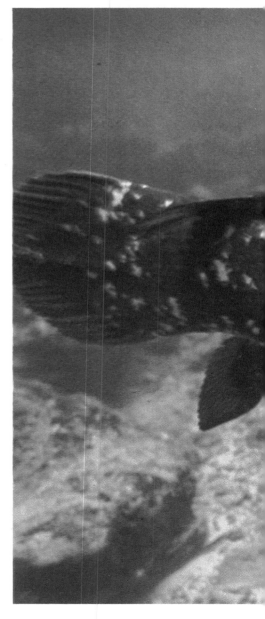

coelacanths have been caught off the islands of Grand Comore and Anjouan at depths between 230 and 1,300ft (70–400m). Most are caught during the first few months of the year in the monsoon season. The two islands are made of highly absorbent volcanic rock and it has been argued, with some possible corroboration from its kidney structure, that the coelacanth lives in areas where the fresh rainwater leaks out into the sea. The coelacanth has the build of a lurking predator and fish remains have been found in the stomach. It has very large eggs: 20 about the size of a tennis ball were found in a 5.3ft (1.6m) long female. The only known embryos, which still had yolk sacs so were probably not close to birth, were more than 12.5in (32cm) long and it has been estimated that the gestation period is well over a year. The females are larger than the males and can live for at least 11 years.

Although the coelacanth is superficially similar to the last known fossilized coelacanths there are some interesting anatomical differences. In the present-day coelacanth, unlike its Cretaceous forebears, the swim bladder is nonfunctional and filled with fat. It retains the peculiar triple tail, the lobed paired fins, a skull with a hinge in it and the rough cosmoid scales of its fossil forebears.

"Anachronisms" do not, as one might have hoped, solve problems—they tend to create more. Why do coelacanths, formerly worldwide, now only live around two small islands? Why have some of the anatomical changes occurred? Why, if they are purportedly freshwater fishes, do they live in the sea? Above all else, how did just one species survive? We will probably never know.

The three genera and six species of **lungfishes** are now confined to the fresh waters of the Amazon, West and Central Africa and the Mary and Burnett Rivers of northern Queensland. Their fossils, by contrast, are found in rocks from Greenland to Antarctica and Australia. As with some other archaic fishes, we know that they represent an important organizational advance somewhere on the march from aquatic vertebrates to land-living vertebrates, but exactly how they fit in is still a matter of some uncertainty.

Living lungfishes are grouped into two families: the South American *Lepidosiren paradoxa* and the African *Protopterus* (4 species) are in the Lepidosirenidae whereas the Australian *Neoceratodus forsteri* is the sole occupant of its family (Ceratodontidae).

Neoceratodus retains more of the primitive features of its Devonian ancestors than do its relatives. It has large scales and lobed, paired fins fringed with rays retaining the primitive characteristic of being more numerous than the supporting bones. The dorsal, caudal and anal fins are confluent. Unlike *Protopterus* (see below) it cannot survive drought and will die if it is out of water for any length of time. The lungs open by a ventral slit in the oesophagus; the air tube then runs dorsally so that the partially two-lobed lungs lie dorsal in a similar position as the swim bladder in bony fishes but not like the lungs in other vertebrates which lie ventral to the alimentary tract. The Australian lungfish normally uses its gills for respiration but also breathes atmospheric air in adverse conditions.

Lungfishes are carnivores, and when fully grown (about 5ft, 1.5m) will eat frogs and small fish. The teeth consist of a pair of sharp plates in each jaw which work in a shearing action.

Reproduction has been observed in shallow water in August when, following a rudimentary courtship consisting of the male nudging the female, the eggs are scattered over a small area of dense weed and fertilized (hopefully). There is no indication of any further parental concern. Although native to two small river systems, the interest in this rare species is such that stocks have been transplanted into other Australian rivers. At least three of the introductions have been successful and the fish have bred.

The biology of the African species is better known. At least two, *Protopterus annectens* from west and southern Africa and *P. dolloi* from the Zaïre basin, are known to survive drought by a type of summer hibernation (aestivation) in cocoons. The widespread East African species *P. aethiopicus* is thought to be capable of aestivating but in the wild rarely does so as its waters are less likely to dry up.

African lungfish are more elongate than their Australian relatives. Small scales cover the body and the paired fins are long and threadlike. They are aggressive predators and can grow to more than 6.5ft (2m) long. The lungs are paired and lie in a ventral position as in terrestrial vertebrates. The use of lungs in breathing here necessitates a four-chambered heart, so unlike bony fish the lungfish's auricle and ventricle are functionally divided by a partition so that blood is circulated to the lungs as a bypass from the normal body and gill circulation.

All the African lungfish make nests. In *Protopterus aethiopicus* it is often a deep hole made by the male who will then guard the newly hatched young for about two

months. As well as driving away would-be predators he also aerates the water in the nest. The nest of *P. dolloi* is much more elaborate and has an underwater entrance. The terminal brood chamber may be in swampy ground and may be open at the top. Aeration vents are also built into it by the male.

The larvae of African (and South American) lungfish have external gills, the degree of development varying with the amount of oxygen in the water. At metamorphosis the external gills are usually resorbed and the lung and gill respiration takes over. Occasionally vestigial external gills remain throughout life.

Protopterus annectens lives in swamps and rivulets that are prone to drying out, often for months. To survive the fish burrows into the soft mud as the water level falls. Using its mouth and general body pressure the lungfish widens out the bottom of the tube until it can turn round. As the water falls below the opening of the tube the fish closes the mouth of the tube with a block of porous mud, curls up in the lower chamber and then secretes much special mucus which hardens to form an encasing cocoon with only an opening for the mouth. The cocoon conserves moisture and the porous mud plug allows breathing. During aestivation, as in hibernation, the metabolic rate is

▲ **An aborigine.** The Australian or Queensland lungfish (*Neoceratodus forsteri*) is native only to rivers in Queensland. Less adapted than its relatives to air breathing, it relies on gill respiration. Its diet includes fish, as here, which it chews with bony plates in the mouth. The Australian authorities have been trying to introduce this exciting fish to other rivers.

▲ **Survival posture** ABOVE RIGHT. At least two of the four species of African lungfishes (genus *Protopterus*) can survive drought by burrowing into mud, sealing themselves off and entering summer hibernation (aestivation). This can last for at least three years, during which time they feed off their own muscle tissue.

► **From familiarity to fame.** Before the coelacanth became known to the scientific world it was familiar to the inhabitants of the Comoro Islands. They called the fish *kombessa*. To them it was valueless. Now the fish has scientific value it is a highly prized catch.

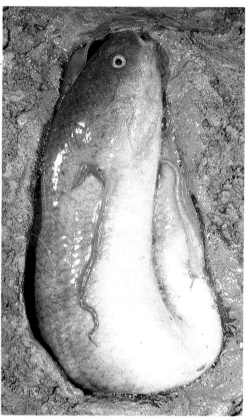

greatly reduced and the basic energy needed for survival comes from the breakdown of muscle tissue. In this state they have been known to survive four years of drought although normally an incarceration of only a few months would be necessary. When the river floods again the waters dissolve the cocoon and the fish emerges.

The South American lungfish (*Lepidosiren*) looks similar to the African with an eel-like body and feeler-like fins. It also possesses the general characteristics of a cartilaginous vertebral column and a common opening for the rectal, excretory and genital products.

Lepidosiren aestivates but its refuge is much simpler than that of its African relatives and no cocoon is produced. An elaborate nest is made in the breeding season during which time the pelvic fins of the male bear a large number of blood-rich filaments. The function of these is unknown, but suggestions have included the release of oxygen into the water of the nest or alternatively acting as supplementary gills to reduce the number of visits to the surface while guarding the young.

KEB

The Finding of the Coelacanth

It is an axiom in biology that absence of records does not imply certainty of extinction.

On a hot summer's day in 1938 Captain Goosen's boat *Nerine* docked at East London in South Africa. At that time Mary Courtnay-Latimer was the curator at the East London Museum and local skippers were accustomed to her frequent visits to the port to obtain fish specimens for the museum. At 10.30am that morning (22 December) she was telephoned and told that the *Nerine* had returned with some specimens for her. Among the catch was a large blue fish with flipper-like fins and a triple tail which she had never seen before. After several attempts she found a taxi driver willing to take her and her 5ft (1.5m) long, oily, smelly prize back to the museum. There, after searching through reference books, the nearest she could come to identifying the fish was as "a lung fish gone barmy."

Realizing that her find was important she tried to contact Dr J. L. B. Smith (whose name will be forever linked with the fish), the ichthyologist at Rhodes University, Grahamstown. It was then mid summer in South Africa; temperatures were high; how was an important oily fish to be preserved? The local mortuary refused to have this corpse in its cold store. Finally a local taxidermist, Mr R. Centre, although admitting inexperience in fish-stuffing, agreed to help. He wrapped the body in cloth, soaked it in formalin and placed it in a makeshift ichthyosarcophagus.

On 26 December there was still no reply from J. L. B. Smith. An examination of the body showed that the formalin had not penetrated and that the internal organs were rotting. Pragmatism dictated that the decaying parts should be thrown away and what could be preserved should be preserved. On 3 January 1939 a telegram arrived from J. L. B. Smith. It read "MOST IMPORTANT PRESERVE SKELETON AND GILLS = FISH DESCRIBED." The ensuing search of local rubbish heaps failed to find the missing organs. Parallel disasters now revealed themselves. The early photographs taken of the fresh fish had been spoiled. The museum trustees, not thinking the fish important, had ordered the skin to be mounted before, on 16 February, J. L. B. Smith finally arrived. He stared at the mounted skin and said: "I always knew, somewhere, or somehow, a primitive fish of this nature would appear."

He described the fish as *Latimeria chalumnae*. The origin of the generic name needs no explanation and it is followed by an allusion to the Chalumna River, off which the fish was purportedly caught.

Why had this conspicuous, spiny-scaled fish remained unnoticed for so long? Its large eye and lurking predator shape suggested it did not normally live off East London. Unless the only specimen had been caught, there must be more, but where?

The chase was long and extremely exciting.

It took 14 years, involved a great deal of work and almost the commandeering of the South African Prime Minister's private aircraft. For all the details the reader is recommended to read J. L. B. Smith's book *Old Fourlegs*.

Just before Christmas 1952 (note the date again), J. L. B. Smith received a telegram from Eric Hunt from the Comoro Islands. It read: "REPEAT CABLE JUST RECEIVED HAVE FIVE FOOT SPECIMEN COELACANTH INJECTED FORMALIN HERE KILLED 20TH ADVISE REPLY HUNT DZAOUDZI." The search had finally come to ground. Dzaoudzi is in the Comoros and there lives the coelacanth.

Although this discovery was very exciting to the scientific community, the natives on the Comoro Islands were unmoved. They knew this fish, had given it the name of Kombessa, and considered it to be a worthless catch although the rough scales could be used in roughing a bicycle tyre tube prior to mending a puncture.

SHARKS

Subclass: Selachii
About three hundred and seventy species in 74
genera, 21 families and 12 orders.
Distribution: worldwide in tropical, temperate
and polar oceans at all depths.

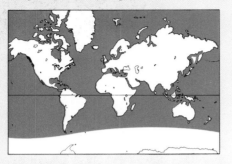

Size: adult lengths 10in–65ft (25cm–20m),
adult weights 1–26,500lb (2–12,000kg).

▲ **A potent image of the modern world,** the
teeth of a Great white shark. With cinema's
need for gripping visual subjects the Great
white shark has, perhaps inevitably, become
one of the great stars of the wide screen.
Celluloid has magnified and popularized this
shark's infamy in a manner only possible in the
contemporary world. Serving a need for
spectacle has however brought distortion and
misrepresentation. The number of deaths
attributable to sharks is minimal, and among
sharks there is a great variety of forms, which
tends to be overlooked. Even teeth vary
considerably: in some sharks teeth for grinding
are predominant; others are filter-feeders.

▶ **Beauty in shape, movement and color,** a
requiem shark (genus *Carcharinus*),
photographed off the Maldive Islands in the
Indian Ocean. Most of the hundred or so species
in the order of requiem sharks are restricted to
the tropics.

Most people think that sharks are large, fast-swimming, elegant savage predators. This is true of some species, but only of a minority. The group should be of general interest on account of the intriguing aspects of biology found within it: all sharks have an exceptional sense of smell; some can detect minute electrical discharges; some sharks give birth to live young.

One of the most notable features of sharks is their teeth. In the large highly predaceous sharks these are large and razor sharp, used for cutting and shredding their prey into bite-sized pieces. However, this is not the case in all species. Bottom-feeding species, which eat mollusks and crustaceans, have teeth flattened for crushing the shells of their prey. Fish-eaters have very long, thin teeth to help them catch and hold on to a struggling and slippery fish. At any one time a shark may have up to 3,000 teeth in its mouth, arranged in 6 to 20 rows, according to species. In most sharks only the first row or two are actively used for feeding. The remaining rows are replacement teeth, in varying stages of formation with the newest teeth being at the back. As a tooth in the functioning row breaks or is worn down it falls out and a replacement tooth moves forward in a sort of conveyor-belt system. A shark can replace its teeth every few days. Thus the functional row, or rows, of teeth are always kept sharp. It has been estimated that a shark may use over 20,000 teeth in its lifetime. The strong jaws of a shark can exert a biting strength of 44,000lb per sq in (3,000kg per sq cm) on the teeth. Contrast this with only 150lb per sq in (10kg per sq cm) in humans.

Sharks find their prey through a number of sensory systems. Many have poor eyesight, but a few, especially the isuroids (eg thresher sharks) and requiem sharks have good eyesight (as good as man's). Some species have sensory barbels around their mouth to taste the sea bed for prey. All sharks have a very keen sense of smell. Their nostrils are used only for smelling, not for breathing. The part of a shark's brain that deals with smelling is twice as large as the rest—evidence of the importance of smell. Sharks can detect one part of blood in a million parts of water—about 1 drop of blood in 25 gallons (115 liters) of water!

Sharks (along with skates and rays and chimaeras) have a lateral line system: a series of canals on the entire body and head which are filled with a jelly-like substance, sensory receptors which pick up pressure waves caused by the movements of another animal or even by the shark itself approaching a stationary object.

On the snout are the so-called ampullae of Lorenzini, a series of electro-receptive pits (named for Stefano Lorenzini, who first studied them in 1678). They are the most sensitive electro-receptive devices found in any animal. They are capable of picking up one-millionth of a volt, which is less than the electric charge produced by the nerves in an animal's body! Thus sharks can find their prey from the prey's natural electric output.

The most primitive living shark is the **Frilled shark**. It has broad-based trident-like teeth which are otherwise found only in fossil sharks. Its common name derives from its long, floppy gill flaps, forming a frill around the head. Its primitive and unique characters place it in its own group. First discovered off Japan on Sagami Bay in the 1880s it was long thought to occur nowhere else. In fact for unknown reasons it only enters water as shallow as 100ft (30m) in Sagami Bay. Recent deep trawling has shown that it lives at depths of 1,000–2,000ft (300–600m) over a wide area off the coasts of Australia, South Africa, Chile, California and Europe. It grows to 6ft (2m) long and has a thin eel-like body. It feeds on small fish swallowed whole. The female develops eggs in her body (ovoviviparous), producing 6–12 young per litter.

The **six- and seven-gilled sharks** are so named because they have developed one or two extra sets of gill slits. They prefer cold water, and in the tropics live in deep water. Individuals have been photographed more than 6,000ft (1,800m) down. Only in cold polar waters do they come into shallow water. They reach 15ft (4.5m) in length and feed on other fishes. Upper-jaw teeth are long and tapered; lower-jaw teeth are short and wide with unique, strong, multiple serrations. They too develop eggs internally and produce up to 40 young.

The horn sharks live in the Indian and Pacific oceans. These sluggish, bottom dwellers, 3ft (1m) long, feed on shallow-water mollusks and crustaceans. The genus name (*Heterodontus*—"different teeth") reflects the fact that, unlike other sharks, they have pointed front teeth and rear teeth adapted into crushing plates. They are rather stout, stocky sharks and have prominent brow ridges above their eyes which give them the appearance of having horns—hence horn sharks. All species are spotted or patterned, making them rather handsome. This, coupled with their small size and hardiness, has resulted in them being desired by aquarists. They are easy to care for and will live for

THE 12 ORDERS OF SHARKS

Frilled shark

Order: Chlamydoselachiformes
Family: Chlamydoselachidae.
Sole species *Chlamydoselachus anguineus*.

Distribution: off coasts of California, Chile, Europe, S Africa, Japan, Australia.

Six- and seven-gilled sharks or hexanchoids

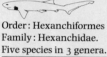

Order: Hexanchiformes
Family: Hexanchidae.
Five species in 3 genera.

Distribution: worldwide in cold marine waters at shallow to moderate depths.

Horn or Port Jackson sharks or heterodontoids

Order: Heterodontiformes
Family: Heterodontidae.
Six species of the genus *Heterodontus*.

Distribution: tropical Pacific Ocean.

Orectoloboids

Order: Orectolobiformes
About thirty species in 12 genera and 5 families.

Distribution: Indo-Pacific Ocean; two species in Atlantic Ocean.
Families, genera and species include: **banded catsharks and epaulette sharks** (family Hemiscyllidae), including **epaulette sharks** (genus *Hemiscyllium*); **carpet sharks** (family Orectolobidae); **catsharks** (family Parascyllidae); **nurse sharks** (family Ginglymostomatidae); **Whale shark** (*Rhincodon typus*, sole species of the family Rhincodontidae).

Catsharks and false catsharks or scylloids

Order: Scyliorhiniformes
Eighty-seven species in 18 genera.
Distribution: worldwide in cold or deep marine water.
Families, genera and species include: **catsharks** (family Scyliorhinidae), including **Lesser spotted dogfish** (*Scyliorhinus caniculus*), **swell sharks** (genus *Cephaloscyllium*); **False catshark** (*Pseudotriakis microdon*, sole species of the family Pseudotriakidae).

Smooth dogfish sharks or triakoids

Order: Triakiformes
Family: Triakidae.
About thirty species in 5 genera.
Distribution: worldwide in tropical, subtropical and temperate seas.
Species include: **Leopard shark** (*Triakis semifasciata*), **Soupfin shark** (*Galeorhinus zyopterus*).

Sand tiger, false sand tiger and goblin sharks or odontaspoids

Order: Odontaspidiformes
Seven species in 3 genera and 3 families.
Distribution: worldwide in tropical and temperate seas.
Families, genera and species include: **False sand tiger shark** (*Pseudo-carcharias kamoharrai*, sole species of the family Pseudocarchariidae); **Goblin shark** (*Scapanorhynchus owstoni*, sole species of the family Scapanorhynchidae); **sand tiger sharks** (genus *Odontaspis*, family Odontaspididae).

Thresher, mackerel and megamouth sharks or isuroids

Order: Isuriformes
Ten species in 6 genera and 3 families.
Distribution: worldwide in tropical and temperate seas.
Families, genera and species include: **mackerel sharks** (family Isuridae), including **Basking shark** (*Cetorhinus maximus*), **Great white shark** or **man-eater** or **White shark** (*Carcharodon carcharias*), **Mako shark** (*Isurus oxyrinchus*), **Porbeagle shark** (*Lamna nasus*), **Salmon shark** (*L. ditropis*); **megamouth sharks** (family Megachasmidae); **thresher sharks** (family Alopiidae).

Requiem sharks or carcharhinoids

Order: Carcharhinoidiformes
Family: Carcharhinidae.
One hundred species in 10 genera.
Distribution: worldwide in tropical and temperate seas.
Species and genera include: **Black-tipped shark** (*Carcharhinus melanopterus*), **Bull shark** (*C. leucas*), **Great hammerhead shark** (*Sphyrna mokarran*), **hammerhead sharks** (genus *Sphyrna*), **Tiger shark** (*Galeocerdo cuvier*), **White-tipped shark** (*Carcharhinus albimarginatus*).

Spiny dogfish and allies or squaloids

Order: Squaliformes
Family: Squalidae.
About seventy species in about 12 genera.
Distribution: worldwide in cold or deep seas.
Species and genera include: **bramble sharks** (genus *Echinorhinus*), **cigar sharks** (genera *Isistius*, *Squaliolus*), **sleeper sharks** (genus *Somniosus*), **Spiny dogfish** (*Squalus acanthias*).

Angelsharks or squatinoids

Order: Squatiniformes
Family: Squatinidae.
About ten species of the genus *Squatina*.
Distribution: worldwide in tropical and temperate seas.

Sawsharks or pristiophoroids

Order: Pristiophoriformes
Family: Pristiophoridae (sawsharks).
Five species in 2 genera.
Distribution: Bahamas, off coast of S Africa, western Pacific Ocean from Japan to Australia.

▶ **Port Jackson shark** ABOVE (*Heterodontus portjacksoni*), a species in the order of horn sharks. These are as distinctive as the more familiar sharks but in their own ways. Their specific features include the horn-like ridges above the eyes, pointed front teeth and crushing plates, and bottom-dwelling habits.

▶ **Among the smallest of the sharks** are those species belonging to the order of catsharks and false catsharks. Most are no larger than 3–4.5ft (1–1.5m). Consonant with their size is their diet, which includes non-fish prey and bottom-dwelling fishes. The swell sharks have developed techniques for defense against predators. This is the Gulf catshark (*Halaelurus vincenti*).

years in captivity. They lay eggs which are unique in shape, having a spiral form. These are forced into crevices between rocks or pieces of coral by the female. The screw shape helps hold the egg in place.

The **orectoloboids** are an order of five closely related families of sharks. They are tropical to subtropical fishes. Only two species are found in the Atlantic Ocean, the rest are in the Indo-Pacific.

In size the orectoloboids range from the epaulette sharks (genus *Hemiscyllium*)—3ft (1m) long—to the Whale shark, which has been reliably reported as reaching over 50ft (15m) in length and is the world's largest fish. In most species the young are born with beautiful spotted or banded patterns, which are lost when they mature.

Most species lay eggs (ie are oviparous), but a few develop them internally (ie are ovoviviparous). Usually less than 12 young are produced per litter.

All species except the Whale shark are bottom dwellers, spending most of their time just sitting on the ocean floor. The skeletons of the pectoral fins are modified so that they can actually use the fins for walking on the ocean floor. Many species, even when disturbed, will crawl away rather than swim.

Most orectolobiform species feed on mollusks and crustaceans and have teeth for crushing and grinding. All have sensory barbels around the mouth. The carpet sharks eat mainly fish, so they have long, thin teeth. The Whale shark is a filter feeder, having its gill arches specially modified to act like a sieve to filter out the planktonic organisms upon which it feeds. As its teeth are redundant they are minute. Its vast bulk needs constant fuel, so the Whale shark swims incessantly, filtering the ocean for its food. A slow swimmer, it has been involved in collisions with boats as it often swims at the surface where there is most food. (Boat and passengers are usually more damaged than the shark.) It is found worldwide, in all tropical and subtropical oceans. Many orectolobiforms are commonly kept by aquarists on account of their small size, hardiness and beautiful patterns.

The **catsharks and false catsharks** comprise about 18 genera and 87 species. Most live in cold or deep waters. They are found worldwide. Many are spotted or patterned and do not lose this coloration as they mature. These stocky forms live on the ocean floor. They feed on mollusks, crustaceans and bottom-dwelling fishes, using their short, stout teeth. Some species have sensory barbels to help them locate their prey.

Most are small, maturing at about 3–4.5ft (1–1.5m). However, some species are larger, eg the False catshark, which is reported to reach 9ft (3m). The swell sharks are aptly named. When frightened or attacked they swallow water or air into their stomachs, enlarging their girth to three or four times its normal size.

The tasteful flesh of catsharks is much appreciated. In England the Lesser spotted dogfish is commonly sold in fish and chip shops under the name of rock salmon or huss.

The **smooth dogfish sharks** (triakoids) live in shallow waters of tropical, subtropical and temperate seas. They are moderately large sharks reaching about 6ft (2m) in length. They are bottom dwelling, feeding upon mollusks, crustaceans and fish, but they do not sit or crawl. The majority of species have modified crushing and grinding teeth.

The Leopard shark from the Eastern Pacific has a beautiful color pattern with dark gray to black spots on a silvery background which makes it a favorite for public aquaria. The Soupfin shark is commercially fished in the Orient for its fins which are used to make shark fin soup.

Virtually all species are migratory, spending winter in the tropics and migrating to temperate waters in the summer. Evidence suggests these migrations are regulated by water temperature. Females of these species develop embryos in the uterus and deliver 10–20 young at a time. Overall the triakoids epitomize the general public's concept of typical sharks.

The **sand tiger**, **false sand tiger** and **goblin sharks** are all fairly large, reaching 10–12ft (3–3.5m) in length. The sand tiger sharks (5 species) are found worldwide in shallow, temperate and tropical waters. Largely fish-eaters, they have the appropriate long, thin teeth. The tooth shape produces an extremely ferocious appearance which, combined with their rather docile nature, has made them favorites in public aquaria, where they can live for over 20 years. (The term sandshark is often, but inaccurately, applied to any smallish shark that comes into shallow water, including sand tiger sharks, smooth dogfish, spiny dogfish, nurse sharks and requiem sharks.)

Reproduction in this order is viviparous, ie embryos develop in the uterus, and quite unusual. The female begins with 6–8 embryos per uterus. As they grow these embryos devour one another until one embryo per uterus is left. Hence only two young are born at a time. This unique prenatal feeding habit is called intra-uterine cannibalism.

The False sand tiger shark lives in deeper waters off China and East and West Africa. One specimen caught off West Africa by the German research vessel *Walther Herwig* gave birth to four young when it was brought on deck. Thus the False sand tiger shark does not seem to have intra-uterine cannibalism. Otherwise very little is known of the biology of this large-eyed fish-eater.

The Goblin shark is perhaps the most bizarre of all living sharks. Projecting from its "forehead" is an extremely long, thin, broad, shovel-shaped process. Its function is unknown. The Japanese fishermen that first caught it called it *tenguzame*, which means "goblin shark." Like the Frilled shark, it was originally caught in the 1890s in Japan's Sagami Bay. Since then it has been caught in the Indian Ocean, off South Africa and off the coast of Portugal at depths of 1,000ft (300m) and more. Again more deep-water collecting will probably extend its known range. In life Goblin sharks are a translucent white color, but become very dark brown soon after death. Judging by its teeth it is a fish-eater. Apart from its length, 14ft (4.3m), we know practically nothing about it.

The **thresher**, **mackerel** and **megamouth sharks** are among the largest sharks in the world. They are found in tropical and temperate seas.

The thresher sharks derive their name from the extremely long, thin upper lobe of their caudal fin, which may be as long as the rest of their body. Swimming into a school of small fishes they use their tail like a whip, thrashing it among the school, killing or stunning the fishes, which are then eaten. They reach a length of about 20ft (6m) and give birth to only a few young, but those of the largest species are about 5ft (1.5m) long! These pelagic sharks rarely come into shallow water.

The most recent exciting shark discovery was that of the aptly named megamouth, which was first described only in 1983. This 15ft (4.5m) long fish—only two are known—was caught accidentally off Hawaii in 1977 in 500ft (150m) of water. It is a filter feeder, but unlike other known filter feeders its mouth has many organs that are thought to be luminous. A second specimen was caught in 1984 off the California coast. How such a large animal has evaded capture is a great mystery.

The family of mackerel sharks contains some of the best known sharks, including the unjustifiably infamous Great white

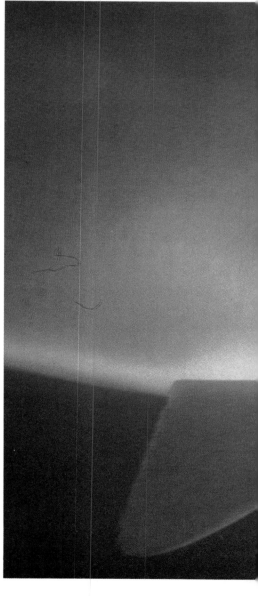

◄ **Poised for emergence,** a dogfish in its egg capsule. In sharks there are three modes of egg development. Most sharks are ovoviviparous, that is eggs develop and hatch in the womb. Several species are viviparous: the eggs develop in the womb connected to the wall by a yolk "placenta." Following the gestation period, the females of ovoviviparous and viviparous shark species give birth to fully developed young. A few species are oviparous: the female lays fertilized eggs. A female dogfish normally lays 18–20 eggs, each measuring about 2 × 4in (5 × 11cm). She deposits them among vegetation or sponges, and each capsule fastens itself to a support with a filament. From laying to hatching normally takes 8–9 months.

▼ **Poised for attack,** a sand tiger shark. The six species of the genus *Odontaspis* live in the tropical and subtropical seas. They grow to 20ft (6m) in length, and are voracious predators. Usually they are sluggish: invigoration appears when the time comes for hunting, and they head for shallow waters.

shark. Also here are the Porbeagle shark, the Mako shark and the Basking shark. The mackerel sharks are large (the Basking shark reaches 30ft, 9m), and live in all tropical and temperate seas.

They all have an unusual caudal fin with the lobes being nearly equal in length, caudal keels on either side of the tail, and are relatively fast swimmers (in part due to the previous two characters). Most species are fish-eaters. Some make spectacular leaps into the air—one of the reasons they are popular game fish. It is not known why they make these leaps, but it has been suggested that it is an attempt to dislodge skin parasites. The Basking shark is known to have collided with boats during such leaps, which have caused numerous human deaths. Most, if not all, species are homeothermic, ie they maintain their body temperature above that of their surroundings.

The Mako shark is probably the fastest fish in the world. It has been recorded to swim at speeds over 60mph (95km/h), and is known to have out-swum and eaten swordfish. Reaching over 20ft (6m) in length, it is a prized catch because its delicious flesh is highly sought after and valuable.

The most famous shark is probably the Great white shark, also called the White pointer, Man eater, White death, or just White shark. It is the species most often cited in references to shark attacks on humans. Mainly feeding on marine mammals (the only shark to do so), its broad, serrated teeth are designed for biting large chunks of flesh from whales and seals. Although cited as reaching about 36ft (12m) in length, authentic records show that it rarely grows over 23ft (7m) in length. It is known to be viviparous, ie embryos develop in the

Shark Attacks

The most famous characteristic of sharks is their alleged propensity to kill and eat humans. But less than one-tenth of all shark species have been implicated in unprovoked shark attacks.

The idea that there is a shark off every beach waiting for people to go into the water so that it can attack them is completely untrue. To put it in perspective, every year thousands more people are killed by other people than by sharks; thousands more people are killed in automobile accidents than by sharks, and more people are killed by lightning than by sharks. Each year humans kill tens of thousands of sharks yet there are fewer than 100 shark attacks upon humans.

The Great white shark, often called the man-eater, has the greatest reputation for attacking humans. Recent studies of Great white sharks show that they mainly feed on sea mammals—seals and porpoises. Seen from below a person swimming looks much like a seal, with arms and legs sticking out. The shark usually surprises its victim, be it man or seal, with one massive bite, and then retreats in order to allow its victim to die before eating it. For this reason many humans survive the

attack of a Great white shark if they are saved before being eaten. Death, however, may result from this one massive bite, from blood loss or damage to organs.

Attacks by other species of sharks, mostly requiem sharks, are for feeding. The most dangerous are the Tiger shark and various species of hammerhead sharks. Large individuals of these species can eat a whole human, whereas smaller ones would only take bites. The only other species that is a confirmed man-eater is the Australian sand tiger shark. Sharks, unlike tigers, do not acquire a taste for human flesh. (Sharks have small brains and cannot "learn." Feeding is instinctive.) Simply, if one of these sharks is hungry and a person is in the water the shark will eat the person just as readily as it will eat anything.

Much research has gone into finding out how to prevent shark attacks. Various chemicals, air bubbles and electric fields have been tried to deter attacks. Some are useless; others will deter some species of sharks but actually attract others! Dr Eugenie Clark has experimented with a skin secretion produced by the Moses sole, found in the Red Sea. This chemical deters attacks by certain sharks, but is not a universal repellent.

uterus, but a pregnant female has never been caught, so there is no information on litter size or the size of young at birth. The smallest free-swimming specimen known was about 3ft (1m) long. Only the belly is white, the dorsal side usually being grayish.

The Porbeagle shark and the Salmon shark are the smallest members of the mackerel sharks family, 9ft (2.7m) long. They live in the Atlantic and Pacific oceans respectively. They are fish-eaters and have an unusual mode of embryo development. Only one embryo develops in each uterus, but instead of eating other embryos, the female produces more infertile eggs during gestation which the two embryos eat for their nourishment.

The Basking shark is second in size to the Whale shark. Commonly over 30ft (10m) long and recorded up to 45ft (15m) long, it is a filter feeder. Its teeth are minute and virtually useless, and modified gill rakers are used for sieving the plankton. Its liver yields vast amounts of oil and the fish has been the subject of local fisheries in the North Atlantic. The Basking shark's name comes from its behavior of often swimming and resting, ie basking, at the surface.

The **requiem sharks** are probably the largest group of living sharks with about 100 species in 10 genera. In body shape and behavior they are the "typical" shark people think of. They reach 10ft (3m) in length and occur in all tropical and temperate seas.

The Bull shark, found worldwide, commonly enters fresh water for lengthy periods and has been found more than 500 miles from the ocean in the Zambesi River and the Mississippi River. Originally sharks from these fresh waters were thought never to enter the ocean and thus to be distinct species and were appropriately named as "Carcharhinus nicaraguensis" and "C. zambeziensis."

All species of Carcharhinus are widespread and in summer will migrate long distances into temperate waters. They have a metallic gray or brown dorsal coloration. Some, however, will have the edges of the fins tipped in white or black, hence the names White-tipped and Black-tipped sharks. Usually feeding and swimming close to the surface, their large triangular first dorsal fin will often be sticking out of the water, a sign that people have closely associated with shark's proximity.

The largest requiem shark, the Tiger shark, reaches over 18ft (6m) in length and is unquestionably one of the most dangerous sharks. As it swims through the water it will swallow anything that it can

◄ **Possible protection for divers,** a ''shark-proof'' suit being tested.

▲ **A threat to marine mammals.** The Great white shark is the only shark known to feed regularly on dolphins, sea lions and other seals. Humans are normally attacked when it mistakes a swimming man or woman for its usual prey.

get down its throat—literally anything, including rolls of tar paper, shoes, gasoline cans, automobile license plates, and cans of paint, not to mention human parts! One of the most unusual cases of this occurred in April 1935 when a Tiger shark 14.5ft (4.4m) long caught off Maroubra Point, New South Wales, Australia, was brought alive to the Coogee Aquarium. Several days later it regurgitated its stomach contents, which included a human arm. It was found that the arm had not been bitten off by the shark but had been cut off at the shoulder with a sharp instrument, probably a knife. From its tattoos and fingerprints the arm was identified as coming from a man who had been reported missing a week earlier. Police theorized that the man had been murdered, dismembered and the pieces scattered at sea. Although a suspect was arrested he was never proven guilty because the arm regurgitated by the shark was the only piece of evidence that the crime had been committed! Young Tiger sharks have dark bands on a silvery gray background, hence their name. The bands fade with age.

The 12 species of hammerhead sharks are so called because of the large lateral expansions of their heads, on which the eyes are set. Except for their unique heads, which define the genus, they are typical requiem sharks. It has been suggested that their hammer-shaped heads aid in streamlining their bodies, or give them a better field of vision, but more research suggests that the elongate head allows for a more extensive electro-detecting system, the ampullae of Lorenzini. The Great hammerhead shark is the largest, growing to more than 15ft (5m) long. Like other requiem sharks it is highly predaceous and has been involved in several attacks on humans.

The **spiny dogfish sharks** are cold-water forms, worldwide in distribution. All develop eggs internally (ovoviviparous), producing about 12 young per litter. In size they range from less than 1ft (30cm) to over 20ft (6m). Many, especially the deepwater species, feed on squid and octopuses.

In the North Atlantic the Spiny dogfish is probably the most abundant shark. Tens of millions of pounds are caught every year; it is an important food fish. Spiny dogfish rarely exceed 3ft (1m) in length, travel in schools and migrate long distances, moving into Arctic waters each summer. Each dorsal fin is preceded by a spine, which has venom-producing tissue at its base. To humans the venom is painful, but not fatal.

Many deepwater species, especially in the genus *Etmopterus*, have light-producing organs along the sides of their body. Speculation is that these organs may attract their prey, deepwater squids, as well as providing camouflage through "counter-illumination." Their eyes are very large and sensitive at low light levels.

The small but very thin cigar sharks (especially genus *Isistius*) have their lower-jaw teeth greatly elongated. They swim up to a larger animal (a fish, squid, or even a cetacean), bite it, and then with a twist of the body cut out a perfectly circular piece of flesh from the prey.

Sleeper sharks, the giants among spiny dogfish sharks, are the only sharks permanently inhabiting the Arctic water. They have been seen under the polar ice cap. They feed upon seals and fishes, and are probably the only sharks to have flesh that is poisonous to both humans and dogs.

The bramble sharks are unusual in having very large, flat dermal denticles widely scattered on the skin, giving them a "brambly" appearance. There are probably two species, one in the Atlantic (*E. brucus*) and one in the Pacific (*E. cookei*). Although large, over 9ft (2.7m) long, their skeleton is uncalcified and so is extremely soft.

The **angelsharks** are unusual, being very flat, and are considered to be more closely related to the skates and rays than to the more "typical" sharks. They grow to more than 6ft (1.8m) in length and there are about 10 species in the genus *Squatina*, found in all tropical to temperate seas. An anterior lobe of the pectoral fins extends in front of their gill slits. They have long, thin

▲ ▶ **Representative species and genera of sharks.** (1) An adult horn or Port Jackson shark (*Heterodontus portusjacksoni*, order Heterodontiformes) (about 10ft, 3m).
(2) A variolated catshark (genus *Parascyllium*, order Orectolobiformes) (about 24in, 60cm).
(3) A Goblin shark (*Scapanorhynchus owstoni*, order Odontaspidiformes) (11ft, 3.3m).
(4) A Frilled shark (*Chlamydoselachus anguineus*, order Chlamydoselachiformes) (6.5ft, 2m).
(5) A sawshark (genus *Pristiophorus*, order Pristiophoriformes) (about 8ft, 2.5m). (6) A six-gilled shark (*Hexanchus griseus*, order Hexanchiformes) (about 20ft, 6m). (7) A luminous deeepwater dogfish (*Etmopterus hillianus*, order Squaliformes) (12in, 30cm).
(8) A False catshark (*Pseudotriakis microdon*, order Scyliorhiniformes) (10ft, 3m). (9) A humantin (*Oxynotus centrina*, order Squaliformes) (3.3ft, 1m).

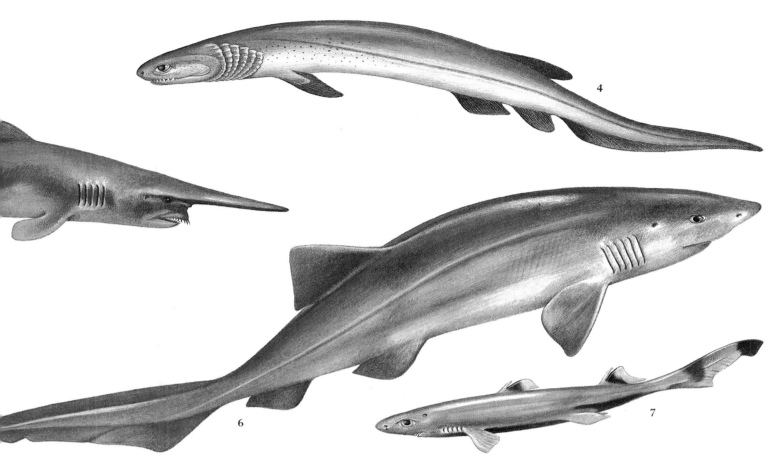

teeth, and sit camouflaged in fairly shallow water, waiting for prey to swim by, when they quickly lunge out and capture it. Usually lethargic, they move very rapidly when catching prey or when they are hooked. If landed on a boat they will snap viciously at anything that comes near, and anything siezed they will hold with great tenacity. They are ovoviviparous, with about 10 young per litter.

Having a long rostrum with lateral rostral teeth very much like a sawfish, the **sawsharks** are true sharks, with lateral gill openings. They are quite rare and grow to a length of about 6ft (1.8m). One species (*Pliotrema warreni*), from the coast of South Africa, has an extra set of gills. The genus *Pristiophorus* has four species, three in the western Pacific, from Japan to Australia in shallow waters, and one Atlantic species found only off the Bahamas in very deep water. They have a pair of long thin barbels under the rostrum which help them find their prey—mollusks and crustaceans—on the sea floor. Their teeth are flat and broad for crushing and their "saws" appear to be used only for defense. Sawsharks are ovoviviparous, producing about 12 young per litter.

GD

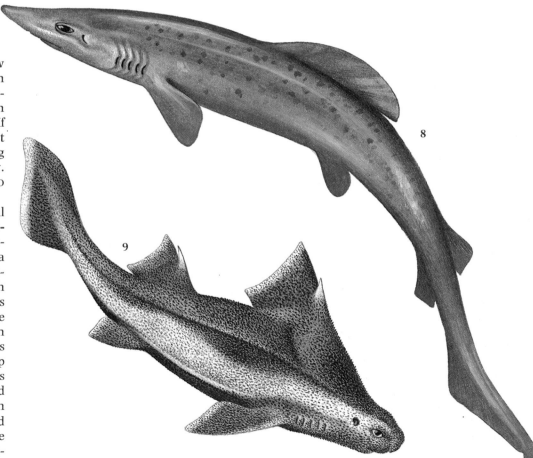

SKATES, RAYS, CHIMAERAS

Order: Batiformes
Skates and rays
About three hundred and eighteen species in
50 genera and 7 families.
Distribution: worldwide in tropical, subtropical
and temperate waters; two genera in fresh
water in S America.

Subclass: Holocephali
Order: Chimaeriformes
Chimaeras
About twenty-three species in 6 genera and
3 families.
Distribution: subarctic, subantarctic, temperate
and tropical waters.

Chimaeras	Skates and rays

▲ **Swan of the oceans,** a Blue-spotted stingray
(*Taeniura lymma*). Found in the Pacific and
Indian Oceans, this species often frequents
shallow waters. Its normal length is about
6.5ft (2m).

▶ **Shark-like sawfish.** ABOVE The distinctive
feature of sawfish is their saw-like snout, which
is similar to that of the hammerhead sharks. It
is a general-purpose adaptation, used for
digging, killing and defense.

▶ **Spread like a butterfly,** a Spotted eagle ray
(*Aetobatus narinari*), a species of eagle ray,
photographed near Christmas Island in the
Pacific. It inhabits tropical and subtropical
shallow waters.

THE mere mention of rayfish to a mariner
conjures up images of gigantic jumping
devilfishes, potently venomous stingarees,
toothy snouted sawfishes and the electric
ray which can stun the unwary: all these
reputations reflect truth and are based on
anatomical adaptations, but human fear
can be excessive. These flattened relatives of
sharks respond defensively to our attempts
to capture and subdue them. Their real contribution to our lives and to the seashore
environment is the role they play as benthic
scavengers, cleaning the bottoms of our
bays and coastal shelves of detritus, and by
their participation in maintaining balance
in the food chain. Although they are bizarre
in appearance, **skates and rays** are edible
and consumed by most fishing cultures.

The order is most closely related to the
angelsharks and sawsharks. All are flattened (one can think of them as "pancake"
sharks), have their pectoral fins extending
well in front of the gill arches and fused to
the sides of the head, and gill slits underneath the body. They are mostly sedentary
and feed on mollusks, crustaceans and
fishes. They have very large openings
(spiracles) which take in the water which
is pumped over the gills and then out
through the ventral gill slits.

Members of the sawfish family are easily
recognized by the large "saw" that pro-
trudes from the front, which is similar to
that of sawsharks. It is used both to capture
food and as a defensive weapon. Swimming
into a school of fishes, sawfish rapidly slash
their saw back and forth, stunning or killing
fish in the school. Then they return and eat
immobile fishes. The razor-sharp teeth on
the saw can cause lethal wounds to an
attacker many times the size of the sawfish.

The number of teeth on the saw varies
with the species and ranges from 12 to 30
pairs. The jaw teeth are short and flattened
for crushing the shells of crustaceans and
mollusks, on which sawfish also feed.
Including the saw, sawfish can reach a
length of about 24ft (7m). The worldwide
Common sawfish is found so often in rivers
and lakes that it has been argued that it is
actually a freshwater species that only
occasionally enters the sea. It even gives
birth in fresh waters. Female sawfish
develop their eggs internally (ovoviviparous), producing up to 12 young per
litter.

Of all the skates and rays, sawfish look
most like sharks, because of their stout
bodies, large dorsal fins and relatively small
pectoral fins.

Species in the guitarfish family look much
like sawfishes without their saws, but have
larger pectoral fins. They range in length
from about 2ft (60cm) for the Atlantic
guitarfish to about 10ft (3m) in the Giant
guitarfish from the Indo-Pacific. They feed
in shallow water on mollusks and crustaceans and have flattened crushing teeth. All
species develop their eggs internally.

The guitarfish genus *Rhinobatos* contains
the largest number of species. Members of
both *Rhinobatos* and *Rhynchobatus* have a
fairly long front extension (rostrum) thus
giving the front part of the body (also called
the disk) a heart-shaped appearance. The
remaining genera (*Rhina*, *Platyrhina*, *Zap-
teryx* and *Platyrhinoides*) have much shorter
rostra and the disk looks round. These four
genera are Indo-Pacific—only *Rhinobatos*
has species in the Atlantic. Many species

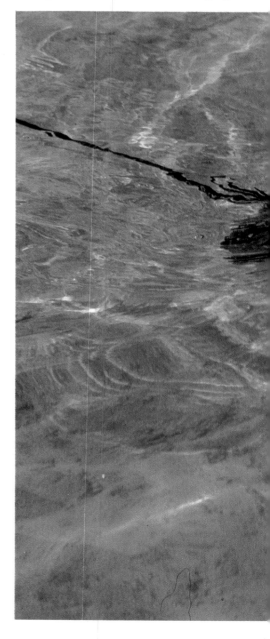

have enlarged dermal denticles, often called thorns, on their dorsal surface.

All members of the electric ray family produce electricity. There are over 30 species in 6 genera, found in all tropical and subtropical seas. Most live in shallow water though a few species are found at great depths. They are slow swimmers, spending most of their time on the ocean bed, and they feed on fishes which they capture by stunning them with electric shocks. Their large electric organs are located at the bases of their pectoral fins and can discharge over 300 volts.

The Lesser electric ray grows to about 1ft (30cm) whereas the Atlantic torpedo ray grows to over 6ft (2m) long and weighs over 200lb (90kg). Their disks are round, the tail short and stubby in most species and the

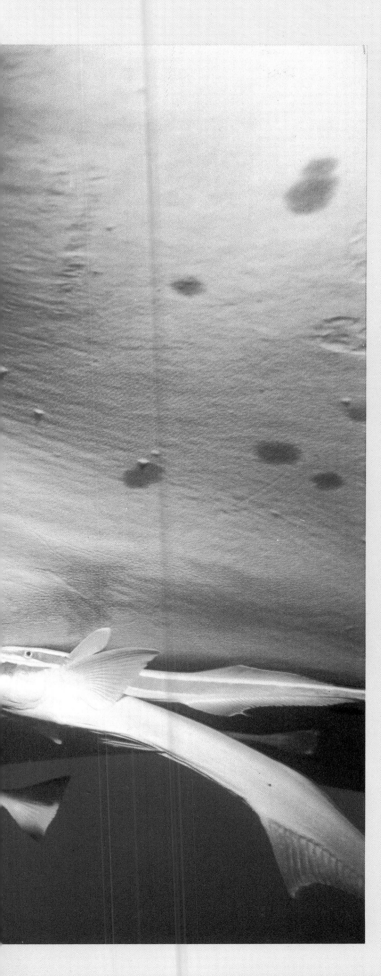

The 7 Families of Skates and Rays

Size: length: 2–24ft (60cm–7m),
weight 1–3,500lb (0.5–1,600kg).

Eagle rays

Family: Myliobatidae
About twenty species in 3 genera.
Distribution: worldwide in tropical
and subtropical oceans.

Electric rays

Family: Torpedinidae
About thirty species in 6 genera.
Distribution: tropical and subtropical
oceans, mainly in shallow water.
Species include: **Atlantic torpedo ray**
(*Torpedo nobiliana*), **Lesser electric ray**
(*Narcine brasiliensis*).

Guitarfish

Family: Rhinobatidae
About thirty-six species in 6 genera.
Distribution: tropical and subtropical
oceans.
Species include: **Atlantic guitarfish**
(*Rhinobatos lentiginosus*), **Giant
guitarfish** (*Rhynchobatus djidensis*).

Mantas

Family: Mobulidae
About eight species in 2 genera.
Distribution: tropical and subtropical
oceans.
Species include: **Atlantic devil ray**
(*Mobula hypostoma*), **Pacific manta**
(*Manta hamiltoni*).

◄ **Fast food.** Giant manta rays
(here *Manta alfredi*) take in food—
small fish and crustaceans—while
on the move. A special adaptation
enables them to sieve food from
the water.

Sawfish

Family: Pristidae
Four species in 2 genera.
Distribution: tropical and subtropical
oceans.
Species include: **sawfish** (*Pristis
pristis*).

Skates

Family: Rajidae
About one hundred and twenty
species in 12 genera.
Distribution: worldwide in cool or
deep-sea waters.
Species include: **Big skate** (*Raja
binoculata*), **Little skate** (*R. erinacea*).

Stingrays

Family: Dasyatidae
About one hundred species in about
19 genera.
Distribution: tropical and subtropical
oceans; two genera in S America
inhabit fresh water. Species include:
Atlantic stingray (*Dasyatis sabina*),
Indo-Pacific stingray (*D. brevicaudata*).

The 3 Families of Chimaeras

Size: length 2–3ft (60–90cm) in most
species to 6–8ft (1.8–2.2m) in
Chimaera monstrosa and *Hydrolagus
purpurescens*; maximum weight 55lb
25kg.

Blunt-nosed chimaeras

Family: Chimaeridae
About thirteen species in 2 genera.
Atlantic, Pacific and Indian oceans.

Long-nosed chimaeras

Family: Rhinochimaeridae
Six species in 3 genera.
Atlantic and Pacific oceans,
Caribbean Sea.

Plow-nosed chimaeras

Family: Callorhinchidae
Four species of the genus
Callorhinchus.
Southern hemisphere.

eyes usually small. In some other species (eg *Typhonarke aysoni* from deep water off New Zealand) there are no functional eyes. The skin is naked in all species and is often beautifully marked. In reproduction eggs develop internally until hatching.

The largest group of skates and rays is the Rajidae family, with about 120 species. They are found worldwide in cool waters— even in the tropics they are common in deep, cold water, at depths greater than 7,000ft (2,100m). Always closely associated with the sea bed, they feed mostly upon mollusks and crustaceans, although they occasionally catch fish. The smallest species is the Little skate, which is common off the Atlantic coast of North America, only reaching about 20in (50cm) long and weighing less than 1lb (450g). The Big skate from the Pacific coast of North America has been recorded at over 8ft (2.5m) and 200lb (90kg).

The enlarged pectoral fins of species in this family and their fairly long snout give the disk a diamond shape. The enlarged pectoral fins of stingrays, eagle rays and manta rays as well as skates are often called wings; and from their graceful up-and-down movements in swimming it is easy to see why. In some skates the pelvic fins have been greatly enlarged and elongated and they can use these to "walk" over the sea bed. The tails of skates are long and thin, and covered with very strong, sharp thorns. The tail, so armed, is used as a defense weapon. Similar thorns or "bucklers" are on the back. The tails have weak electric organs, the four-volt impulses of which may play a part in courtship.

They lay leathery rectangular egg cases with long tendrils at each corner for anchoring to seaweed or rocks. Often washed up, the egg cases are popularly known as "mermaids' purses." The young take 6–9 months to hatch.

Stingrays derive their name from the one or more spines on the dorsal side of their tail. They are found worldwide in warm tropical and subtropical waters, some migrating into temperate waters in the summer. They spend a lot of time camouflaged on the seabed, often partially covered by sand. They can swim rapidly when disturbed, or in pursuit of fish. They also eat mollusks and crustaceans, and have flat, crushing teeth. The disk can be diamond shaped or almost round, causing a distinction between the round stingrays and the square stingrays. Two genera are called butterfly rays (*Gymnura* and *Aetoplatea*) with reference to their wide wings and short, stubby tails.

The spines on stingrays' tails are associated with venom sacs. The venom is very painful but rarely fatal to humans. The needle-sharp spines are used only for defense; each has angled barbs, which allow easy penetration, but make it very difficult to remove.

The Atlantic stingray measures only about 1ft (30cm) across its disk. The largest species is the Indo-Pacific Smooth stingray, which weighs over 750lb (340kg) with a total length of over 15ft (4.5m) and a disk width of over 7ft (2m). Several deaths have been attributed to this species in Australia. Even very large specimens will lie in water less than about 3ft (90cm) deep. Bathers swimming over them have been impaled in the chest or abdomen by the stingray's large spine, up to 1ft (30cm) long, and have subsequently died.

Although most species are marine, there are two South American genera that live only in fresh water (*Potamotrygon* and *Disceus*). Their internal physiology has so adapted to fresh water that if they are placed in salt water they rapidly die. They have an almost perfectly circular disk and are all beautifully marked with spots and bars. Lying in shallow water, covered by mud, they are greatly feared by the native indians because of their poisonous spines. Like all other stingrays, the females develop their eggs internally, producing up to twelve young per litter.

Although they have firm and tasty flesh, stingrays are very rarely eaten. However, their tail spines are commonly sold as curios, especially as letter openers.

The eagle rays are so called because of their very large pectoral wings. When seen from the front they look like eagles flying through water. There are three genera (*Myliobatus*, *Aetobatus* and *Rhinoptera*), found worldwide in tropical and subtropical seas, with about 20 species.

They have no frontal protrusion (rostrum), giving their head a very pugnosed appearance. Their whip-like tail may be more than twice the length of their disk, with one or more spines at the base of the tail. The wings taper and are pointed at the tips, and both the eyes and vents (spiracles) are very large. The teeth are fused into large crushing tooth plates. They eat shellfish, which are found by squirting water from the mouth and blowing away the sand. Such excavations can be 1ft (30cm) deep. Only the soft flesh is swallowed; the crushed shells are spat out. Eagle rays can swim fast enough to take off and glide through the air. Why they do this is unknown. A large shoal can contain several hundred eagle rays.

▲ **Yellow stingrays** (*Urolophus jamaicensis*) shoaling in the Galapagos Islands.

▶ **This leathery disk** is a Thorny ray (*Urogymnus asperrimus*), one of the hundred species of stingray. Stingrays are found in all oceans, usually in waters less than 330ft (100m) deep, and are most abundant close to shore.

▼ **Blunt-nosed chimaeras** or ratfishes live in cold waters in the North Atlantic, off South Africa, and in the Pacific. The first dorsal fin is linked to a poison gland. This is *Hydrolagus colliei*.

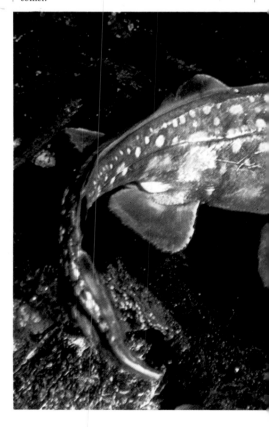

The manta rays are the giants of the skates and rays. The Pacific manta reaches a wingspan of over 20ft (6m) and a weight of over 3,500lb (1,600kg), whereas the wingspan of the Atlantic devil ray is only 5ft (1.5m). Worldwide in tropical and subtropical seas, there are two genera (*Manta* and *Mobula*) and about 8 species.

They have two fins that project forwards from the head, which look like horns—hence the common name of devil-fish. They are truly inhabitants of the open sea, where they swim by flapping their strong pectoral wings. Occasionally they will float at the surface, apparently "basking." Like eagle rays they can swim at great speed and can make spectacular leaps into the air. It has been suggested that they leap either to knock off parasites or to stun schools of small fish just under the water's surface. There have also been several reports of females giving birth to their young during such leaps. (The young develop by feeding upon uterine "milk," like the eagle rays.) The tail is long and whip-like, sometimes with spines at its base. The back is a uniform dark gray to black, while the underside is pure white. Like some of the other giants they are filter feeders, sifting plankton and small fish out of the water by means of special modifications of the gill arches as they swim along. They travel in small groups. Although they are not commercially fished, one individual would provide a large quantity of meat.

A large, blunt head, incisor-like teeth at the front of the mouth, a spine with a venom-producing sac at its base and an elongate tail are some characteristics of the group of fish known as **chimaeras**. Their form recalls the she-monster of Greek mythology (which had a lion's head, a goat's body and a serpent's tail) from which the name chimaera is derived. These relations of the sharks are also known as ratfish or rabbit fish; indeed one of the generic names (*Hydrolagus*) literally means water (*hydros*) rabbit (*lagus*).

All chimaeras occur in cold water, living in subarctic waters or subantarctic waters, often at great depths—some have been recorded as deep as 8,000ft (2,400m). They are poor, slow swimmers. Instead of using powerful side-to-side body movements like most fishes, especially sharks, they swim by flapping their pectoral fins, which makes them bob up and down in an awkward and clumsy fashion. Chimaeras usually keep close to the bottom. They have been observed motionless on the bottom, sitting up on the tips of their fins.

Like all other cartilaginous fishes (sharks, rays etc), males have pelvic claspers to introduce sperm into the female. However, male chimaeras also have a unique clasper projecting from the middle of the forehead which, it is believed, helps to hold the female during mating. Long-nosed and plow-nosed chimaeras have very elongated, fleshy, flexible and unusually shaped head projections (rostra) which are heavily covered with electrical and chemical receptors, possibly used to help locate prey or breeding partners.

All the teeth are fused together to form a solid beak, like that of a bird or turtle, which is used to crush the shells of their food, bottom-dwelling mollusks and crustaceans.

Young chimaeras are covered by short, stout dermal denticles (minute teeth) which are lost as they mature, except in long-nosed chimaeras which keep some of them for life.

Chimaeras have very large, iridescent, metallic blue-green eyes, whose form relates to the low light levels at the depths where they live.

All chimaeras lay fairly large eggs (6–10in, 15–25cm) with a hard leathery shell. They hatch in about 3 months. It is thought they lay only two eggs at a time, one from each uterus.

Sharks take water in through the mouth to pass over the gills and absorb the oxygen they require. Chimaeras do not take in water through their mouths but through large nostrils connected to special channels which direct the water to the gills (see also p12). Unlike sharks, chimaeras have their gills in a common chamber protected by a flap (operculum).

The first dorsal fin of the chimaeras is preceded by a freely movable spine, which is linked to a poison gland that produces venom reported to be painful to humans. The first dorsal fin is short and high; the second is long and low, and gently merges into the long, tapering caudal fin forming, in many species, a filamentous "whip" as long as, or longer than, the rest of the body. Only the plow-nosed chimaeras have an anal fin. In members of the genus *Chimaera* what appears to be a long, low anal fin is merely a fold of skin.

The flesh of chimaeras is very solid and tasty, but they are rarely eaten except in New Zealand and China, though in some parts of the Atlantic seaboards the flesh is appreciated for its strong laxative effect. In Scandinavia they are caught mainly for their liver oil, which is used for medical purposes and as a lubricant. GD

BIBLIOGRAPHY

The following list of titles indicates key reference works used in the preparation of this volume and those recommended for further reading.

Fish Classification

Berg, L. S. (trans. Edwards, J. W.) (1947) *Classification of Fishes both Recent and Fossil*, Ann Arbor, Michigan.

Greenwood, P. H., Miles, R. S., Patterson, C. (eds) (1973) *Interrelationships of Fishes*, Linnean Society of London.

Greenwood, P. H., Rosen, D. E., Weitzman, S. H. and Myers, G. S. (1966) "Phyletic Studies of Teleostean Fishes with a Provisional Classification of Living Forms," *Bulletin of the American Museum of Natural History*, vol 131 (4) pp339–456.

Jordan, D. S. (1963) *The Genera of Fishes and a Classification of Fishes*, Stanford University Press, Stanford, California.

Lindberg, D. U. (1974) *Fishes of the World*, John Wiley and Sons, New York.

Moy-Thomas, J. A. and Miles, R. S. (1971) *Palaeozoic Fishes*, Chapman and Hall, London.

Nelson, J. S. (1984) *Fishes of the World* (2nd edn), John Wiley and Sons, New York.

Norman, J. R. (1966) *A Draft Synopsis of the Orders, Families, and Genera of Recent Fishes and Fish-like Vertebrates*, British Museum (Natural History), London.

General Fish Biology

Alexander, R. McN. (1967) *Functional Designs in Fishes*, Hutchinson, London.

Berra, T. M. (1981) *An Atlas of the Distribution of the Freshwater Fish Families of the World*, University of Nebraska Press, Lincoln, Nebraska, and London.

Boulenger, G. A. and Bridge, T. W. (1910) *Fishes* (vol VII of *The Cambridge Natural History*), Cambridge University Press, London.

Goodrich, E. S. (1909) *Cyclostomes and Fishes* (part IX, fascicle I of Lankaster, R. (ed) *A Treatise on Zoology*), London.

Hoar, W. S. and Randall, D. J. (eds) (1969–) *Fish Physiology*, Academic Press, London and New York.

Marshall, N. B. (1954) *Aspects of Deep Sea Biology*, Hutchinson, London.

Marshall, N. B. (1979) *Development in Deep Sea Biology*, Blandford Press, Poole, Dorset.

Marshall, N. B. (1971) *Explorations in the Life of Fishes*, Harvard University Press, Cambridge, Massachusetts.

Marshall, N. B. (1965) *The Life of Fishes*, Weidenfeld and Nicolson, London.

Norman, J. R. (1975) *A History of Fishes* (3rd edn, revised by Greenwood, P. H.), Ernest Benn, London.

Norman, J. R. and Fraser, F. C. (1937) *Giant Fishes, Whales and Dolphins*, Putnam, London.

Nikolsky, G. V. (1963) *The Ecology of Fishes*, Academic Press, London.

Regional Fish Field Guides and Identification

Arnoult, J. (1959) *Faune de Madagascar: Poissons des eaux douces*, Institut de Recherche Scientifique, Tananarive.

Beaufort, L. F. de *et al* (1913–62) *Fishes of the Indo-Australian Archipelago* (10 vols), E. J. Brill, Leiden.

Boulenger, G. A. (1908–16) *Catalogue of the Freshwater Fishes of Africa* (4 vols), British Museum (Natural History), London.

Clemens, W. A. and Wilby, G. V. (1961) "Fishes of the Pacific Coast of Canada," *Bulletin of the Fisheries Research Board of Canada*, vol 68.

Day, F. (1875–78) *Fishes of India*, Dawson, London.

Fowler, H. W. (1936) "The Marine Fishes of West Africa," *Bulletin of the American Museum of Natural History*, vol 70, pp1–1,493.

Hoese, H. D. and Moore, H. D. (1977) *Fishes of the Gulf of Mexico, Texas, Louisiana and Adjacent Waters*, Texas A. & M. University Press, College Station, Texas.

Jayaram, K. C. (1981) *The Freshwater Fishes of India, Pakistan, Bangladesh and Sri Lanka*, Sri Aurobindo Press, Zoological Survey of India, Calcutta.

Khalaf, K. T. (1962) *The Marine and Freshwater Fishes of Iraq*, Ar-Rabitta Press, Baghdad.

Kumada, T. (ed) (1937) *Marine Fishes of the Pacific Coast of Mexico*, Nissan Fisheries Institute, Odawara, Japan.

Lake, J. S. (1971) *Freshwater Fishes and Rivers of Australia*, Thomas Nelson, Melbourne.

Leim, A. H. and Scott, W. B. (1966) "Fishes of the Atlantic Coast of Canada," *Bulletin of the Fisheries Board of Canada*, vol 155, pp1–485.

Munro, I. S. R. (1967) *The Fishes of New Guinea*, Department of Agriculture, Stock and Fisheries, Port Moresby, Papua New Guinea.

Nichols, J. T. (1943) *Freshwater Fishes of China*, American Museum of Natural History, New York.

Smith, J. L. B. and Smith, M. M. (1963) *The Fishes of Seychelles*, Department of Ichthyology, Rhodes University, Grahamstown, S.A.

Wheeler, A. C. (1969) *The Fishes of the British Isles and Northwest Europe*, Macmillan, London.

GLOSSARY

Adaptation features of an animal which adjust to its environment. Adaptations may be genetic, ie produced by evolution and hence not alterable within the animal's lifetime, or they may be phenotypic, ie produced by adjustment on the behalf of the individual and may be reversible within its lifetime.

Adipose fin a fatty fin behind the rayed DORSAL FIN, normally rayless (exceptionally provided with a spine or pseudorays in some catfish).

Adult a fully developed and mature individual, capable of breeding but not necessarily doing so until social and/or ecological conditions allow.

Air bladder see SWIM BLADDER.

Algae very primitive plants, eg epilithic algae, algae growing on liths (ie stones).

Ammocoetes the larval stage of the lamprey.

Anadromous of fish that run up from the sea to spawn in fresh water.

Brood sac or pouch a protective device made from fins or plates of one or other parent fish in which the fertilized eggs are placed to hatch in safety.

Cartilage gristle.

Caudal fin the "tail" fin.

Caudal peduncle a narrowing of the body in front of the caudal fin.

Cerebellum a part of the brain.

Cilia tiny hair-like protrusions.

Class a taxonomic level. The main levels (in descending order) are Phylum, Class, Order, Family, Genus, Species.

Cogener a member of the same genus.

Colonial living together in a COLONY.

Colony a group of animals gathered together for breeding.

Conspecific a member of the same species.

Cryptic camouflaged and difficult to see.

Ctenoid scales scales of "advanced" fishes which have a comb-like posterior edge, thereby giving a rough feeling.

Cutaneous respiration breathing through the skin.

Cycloid scales scales with a smooth posterior (exposed) edge.

Denticle literally a small tooth; used of dermal denticles, ie tooth-like scales (all denticles are dermal in origin).

Diatoms small planktonic plants with silicaceous tests (shells).

Diomorphism the existence of two distinctive forms.

Disjunct distribution geographical distribution of taxons that is marked by gaps. Many factors may cause it.

Display any relatively conspicuous pattern of behavior that conveys specific information to others, usually to members of the same species; often associated with courtship but also in other activities, eg "threat display."

Dorsal fin the fin on the back.

Endostyle a complex hairy (ciliated) groove that forms part of the feeding mechanism of the larval lamprey.

Epigean living on the surface. See also HYPOGEAN.

Esca the luminous lure at the end of the ILLICIUM (the fishing rod) of the angler fishes.

Family either a group of closely related species or a pair of animals and their offspring. See CLASS and Introduction.

Feces excrement from the digestive system passed out through the anus.

Fin in fishes the equivalent of a leg, arm or wing.

Fin girdles bony internal supports for paired fins.

Ganoid scales a primitive type of thick scale.

Gape the width of the open mouth.

Genus the lowest taxonomic grouping. See CLASS and Introduction.

Gills the primary respiratory organs of fish. Basically a vascularized series of slits in the PHARYNX allowing water to pass and effect gas exchange. The gills are the bars that separate the gill slits.

Gill slits the slits between the gills that allow water through.

Gular plates bony plates lying in the skin of the "throat" between the two halves of the lower jaw in many primitive and a few living bony fishes.

Heterocercal a tail shape in which the upper lobe is longer than the lower and into which the upturned backbone continues for a short distance.

Hypogean living below the surface of the ground, eg in caves.

Illicium a modified dorsal fin ray in angler fishes which is mobile and acts as a lure to attract prey.

Introduced of a species which has been brought from lands where it occurs naturally to lands where it has not previously occurred. Some introductions are natural but some are made on purpose for biological control, farming or other economic reasons.

Invertebrates animals lacking backbones, eg insects, crustacea, coelenterates, "worms" of all varieties, echinoderms, etc.

Krill small shrimp-like marine crustaceans which are an important food for certain species of seabirds, whales and fish.

Lamellae plate-like serial structures (eg gill lamellae) usually of an absorbent or semipermeable nature.

Larva a pre-adult form unlike its parent in appearance.

Lateral line organs pressure-sensitive organs lying in a perforated canal along the side of the fish and on the head. They, as it were, feel at a distance.

Maxillary bone the posterior bone of the upper jaw. Tooth-bearing in primitive fish, it acts as a lever to protrude the tooth-bearing anterior bone (premaxilla) in advanced fish.

Metamorphosis a dramatic change of shape during the course of ontogeny (growing up). Usually occurs where the adult condition is assumed.

Mollusk a shellfish.

Monotypic the sole member of its genus.

Natural selection the process whereby individuals with the most appropriate ADAPTATIONS are more successful than other individuals, and hence survive to produce more offspring. To the extent that the successful traits are heritable (genetic) they will therefore spread in the population.

Neoteny a condition in which a species becomes sexually mature and breeds whilst still in the larval body form, ie the adult body stage is never reached.

Niche the position of a species within the community, defined in terms of all aspects of its life-style (eg food, competitors, predators and other resource requirements).

Olfactory sac the sac below the nostrils containing the olfactory organ.

Opercular bones the series of bones including the operculum (gill flap) and its supports.

Operculum the correct name for the bone forming the gill flap.

Order a level of taxonomic ranking. See CLASS and Introduction.

Osmosis the tendency for ions to flow through a semipermeable membrane from the side with the greatest concentration to the side with the least. This means that in the sea fish fluids pick up ions and have to get rid of them whereas in fresh water retention of vital ions is essential.

Oviparous egg-laying.

Ovipositor a tube by which eggs are inserted into small openings and cracks.

Ovoviviparity the retention of eggs and hatching within the body of the mother.

Pelvic girdle the bones forming the support for the pelvic fins.

Perianal organ an organ around the anus.

pH a measure of the acidity or alkalinity of water: pH7 is neutral; the lower the number the more acid the water and vice versa.

Pharyngeal teeth teeth borne on modified bones of the gill arches in the "throat" of the fish.

Pharynx that part of the alimentary tract that has the gill arches.

Photophore an organ emitting light.

Piscivore fish-eater.

Plankton very small organisms and larvae that drift passively in the water.

Predator an animal that forages for live prey; hence "anti-predator behavior" describes the evasive actions of prey.

Prehensile capable of being bent and/or moved.

Rostrum snout.

Scale a small flat plate forming part of the external covering of a fish; hence deciduous scale, a scale that easily falls off the fish.

Scutes bony plates on or in the skin of a fish.

Spawning the laying and fertilizing of eggs, sometimes done in a spawning ground.

Specialist an animal whose life-style involves highly specialized stratagems, eg feeding with one technique on a particular food.

Species a population, or series of populations which interbreed freely, but not with others. See CLASS and Introduction.

Spiracle a now largely relict GILL SLIT lying in front of the more functional gill slits.

Subcutaneous canal a canal passing beneath the skin.

Swim bladder or air bladder. A gas- or air-filled bladder lying between the gut and the backbone. It may be open via a duct to the PHARYNX so that changes of pressure can be accommodated by exhalation of atmospheric air. If closed, gas is secreted or excreted by special glands. Its main function is buoyancy but it can also be used, in some species, for respiration, sound reception, or sound production.

Teleosts a group of fishes, defined by particular characters. The fishes most familiar to us are almost all teleosts.

Temperate zone an area of climatic zones in mid latitude, warmer than the northerly areas, but cooler than subtropical areas.

Territory area that a fish considers its own and defends against intruders.

Tropics strictly an area lying between 22.5°N and 22.5°S. Often, because of local geography, animals' habitats do not match this area precisely.

Tubercles small keratized protrusions of unknown and doubtless different functions which are either permanent or seasonally or irregularly present on the skin of fish.

Type species the species on which the definition of a genus depends.

Vascularized possessed of many small, usually thin-walled, blood vessels.

Velum a hood around the mouth of larval lampreys (ammocoetes) that is a feeding adaptation.

Vertebrate an animal with a backbone primitively consisting of rigidly articulating bones.

Villi small hair-like processes that often have an absorptive function.

Viviparous producing live offspring from within the body of the mother.

Vomerine teeth teeth carried on the vomer, a median bone near the roof of the mouth.

Weberian apparatus a modification of the anterior few vertebrae in ostariophysan fishes (carps, catfish, characins etc) that transmit sound waves as compression impulses from the SWIM BLADDER to the inner ear thereby enabling the fish to hear.

INDEX

A **bold number** indicates a major section of the main text, following a heading: a ***bold italic*** number indicates a fact box on a group of species: a single number in (parentheses) indicates that the fish name or subject are to be found in a boxed feature and a double number in (parentheses) indicates that the fish name or subject are to be found in a special spread feature. *Italic* numbers refer to illustrations.